ONE WEEK LOAN

Managing Change
in
Manufacturing Systems

Managing Change
in
Manufacturing Systems

JOHN BRANDON

Productivity Publishing
Olney, Bucks, UK

© **1992 Productivity Europe Limited**
Buckinghamshire, UK.

ISBN 1-8741530-00-8

1000295076

Contents

Acknowledgements   i x

Preface   x i

Introduction   xvii
Aims and Objectives   xvii
Market Awareness   xix

Context   xxv

1   The Practice of Management   1
Checklists for Good Management   1
The Technically Progressive Firm   1
Criteria for Survival   3
The Techniques of Delegating   4

2   System Modelling   7
Some Basic Concepts   7
Graphical Representations   7
Metaphors for System Topology and Attribution   9
Choice of Topology and Networking Protocol   15
Alternative Topologies   18

3   Technical Change and Corporate Culture   23
The Nature of Technical Change   23
The Need for Change   25
Cultural Considerations   28
Pressures for Change and Change Agents   30
Internal Pressures   34

Managerial Pressures 35
Technological Pressures 44

4 Structure of the Manufacturing Enterprise 51
Management Structure 51
Devolution to Strategic Business Units (SBUs) 54

5 Changes in the Organization of Manufacture 69
Organizational Structure 72
Change Strategy 73
Management Structure – Devolution Strategies 80
Modular Organization of Production
  – Group Technology (GT) 87
Modular Organization of Production
  – Flexible Manufacturing Systems 93
Modular Middle Management – the Missing Tier 96
Management Philosophy 101
Just-In-Time (JIT) 103
Total Quality Control 106
Implications for Customer-Supplier Relationships
  – Managing the Supply Chain 108

**6 Financial Aspects of Managing Change
   in Manufacturing Systems 117**
Costing Systems for Management of
   Manufacturing Systems 118
Justifying Investment in Manufacture 123
Quantifying Intangible Benefits 130
Financing Change 132
Relevance Regained – Activity Costing Procedures 140

7 Exploiting Resources to the Full 145
Skill Inventory 146
Sources of Short-term Support 152

**8   A Case Study: Production Control
         in the Small Company**   **155**
Scope: Production Control, CAPM and CIM   155
The Developing Company: A Common Profile   157
Fads and Panaceas   160
Self Awareness   161
Planning for Change   163
Anticipating the Pitfalls   164
The Benefits   165
Package or Bespoke?   165
Role of the Consultant   167

9   Managing Information   **171**
Computer-Integrated Manufacture   173
Eliminating the Computer   177
OPT   179

10 Managing Technology   **183**
Managing Technological Uncertainty   186
Polarization of Strategy   187
Developing Technology Strategy   188
Quality of Investment in Manufacturing Systems 191

Acknowledgements

The author is indebted to the large number of industrial companies whose travails have provided material for this work. Unfortunately listing them by name would tend to associate them, in the reader's mind, with the adverse aspects of the work, without necessarily giving credit to the positive values of their operations.

Much of the analysis is based on the interpretation of the work of the author's research associates and students. Particular mention is due to G Q Huang, Nick Ajderian, Richard Raybould, Sarah Green, Chris Thomas and Heiko Schafer.

The author is grateful to the Council of the Institution of Mechanical Engineers for permission to reproduce the illustrations by B W Small, from the Proceedings of the Institution 1983 (figure 6.1), by A K Gill, from the Proceedings of the Institution 1986 (figures 5.1 and 5.2), by M R Hoffman and P G Catton, from the conference on 'Planning for Automated Manufacture' 1986 (figure 6.4), and by M W Dale and P Johnson, from the conference on 'UK Research in Advanced Manufacture' 1986 (figures 9.1 and 9.2).

The author wishes to acknowledge with gratitude permission from Ingersoll Engineers to reproduce the illustrations from their report *Competitive Manufacturing – The Quiet Revolution* (figures 5.3, 5.4, 7.1, 7.2 and 10.1).

Preface

"I heard a good man say, 'Once in seven years I burn all my sermons; for it is a shame if I cannot write better sermons now than I did seven years ago' " John Wesley.

The fundamental problems of Manufacturing Systems may be summarized as providing the

Right Product,
           at a
Competitive Price
           and
On Time.

Many of the problems are, therefore, timeless, involving the simultaneous management of manpower, machinery, methods, materials and money, as shown in Figure P.1. As a consequence, there are many good texts which describe the basic problems of the management of Manufacturing Systems. It might be thought, therefore, that the current text is merely repeating material available elsewhere. What do change, however, are the techniques and tools used in the solution of these problems. The pace of this change has accelerated markedly, as a result of the conditions in markets, technological advances and new thinking in management theory.

Perhaps the most dramatic events have been those relating to the marketplace. A substantial proportion of the popular management literature has been concentrated on the personalities of the most newsworthy marketing entrepreneurs. It must be recognized, however, that much of this literature is extremely ephemeral. For example, a book published in late 1989/early

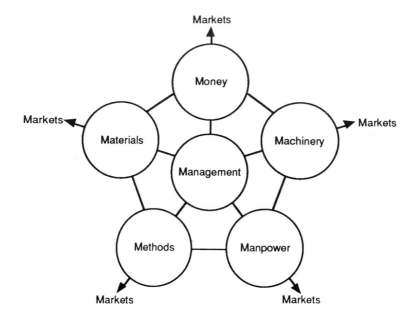

Figure P-1. Management of Manufacturing Systems

1990, described the careers of thirteen entrepreneurs. Presumably the book was written in the early part of 1989. Of these thirteen subjects, just one year later by April 1990, one had been displaced in a boardroom coup, one had departed voluntarily, as a condition for the company's bankers' provision of further support to the company, another's company was already in administrative receivership and another had seriously considered returning his company to private ownership because of his distrust of the short-termism of the financial markets.

This work is intended to provide a synthesis of two hitherto largely distinct categories of texts concerning the management of engineering enterprises. The first, primarily technologically based, are written by Engineers for Engineers. The second, oriented towards general management, concentrate largely on the non-technical aspects of Manufacturing Systems, for example human relations problems, control of information flow, investment planning, etc.

The former category often assumes a technological background in their readership and may, in consequence, be inaccessible to readers without a substantial technical element in their training. Since this accounts for the overwhelming majority of the employees in enterprises concerned with Manufacturing Systems, and, in particular the principal decision makers in the majority of companies, the understanding of the technological aspects of the organization of the business cannot be guaranteed in the management of the change in Manufacturing Systems; this is likely to lead to serious defects in corporate planning. For example, for reasons which will be explained, senior management at MAZAK, perhaps the most successful machine tool builders in recent history, believe that their corporate strategy would have been impossible if they had been a publicly quoted company (Kuba [1]).

In contrast, the latter type of text often assumes (perhaps implicitly) a minimal level of numeracy on the part of the reader, with technological issues presented in the most simplistic of terms. Books aimed at the popular market are often confusing and contradictory. Used uncritically, they are likely to cause mayhem, without any guarantee of the eventual success of any changes in the management behaviour and organization of the company. At the other extreme, many of the more scholarly works are (apparently deliberately) abstract to the point of impenetrability.

Peter Drucker, one of the most influential writers on management, expressed the problem in the following terms:

'... specialization is becoming an obstacle to the acquisition of knowledge and an even greater barrier to making it effective. Academia defines knowledge as what gets printed. But surely this is not knowledge, it is raw data. Knowledge is information that changes something or somebody – either by becoming grounds for action, or by making an individual (or an institution) capable of different and more effective action.' Drucker [2].

There is a substantial middle ground, however, typified by authors such as Heller [3], Crosby [4], Porter [5], Oakland [6] and Kanter [7]. With relatively few exceptions, (for example Harvey-Jones [8]) memoirs of senior executives are of value as case studies in vanity, self delusion and self aggrandisement, which leave the reader in a state of wonderment that any business could thrive under such leadership. Matthew Lynn, of *Business* magazine, summarized the contributions of the entrepreneurial autobiography as follows:

'Books by tycoons are generally a slog to read, partly because they cannot write, and partly because they are so po-faced and serious about every limp thought that wanders into their heads. ' (Lynn [9]).

He concludes that the memoirs of Donald Trump were 'too bad to be true' and, consequently, were a brilliant 'subversive and absurdist parody. '

Much of the material published on the design and operation of Manufacturing Systems is motivated by objectives related to the marketing of products or services, rather than their intrinsic value or direct profit. A significant proportion of the literature has its origins, if not its final form, as promotional material produced by equipment builders, software houses and consultancies. When expressed in these terms, it can be seen that there is likely to be a bias towards the description only of successful implementations, since it makes little commercial sense for companies to publicize their failures. Similarly the limitations of particular management strategies may be minimised by consultancies closely identified with that particular methodology.

The majority of existing texts concentrate (understandably) on the theory of Manufacturing Systems. There is however a substantial volume of research literature that reveals that the uptake of Advanced Manufacturing Technology falls far short of the hopes and expectations of the theorists. The text presents a (hopefully) balanced treatment which compares the theoretical potential of manufacturing systems with their practical realizations, explaining the reasons for the shortfall. A particular feature of the text is an assessment of the effects of financial appraisal methodologies.

The book is intended to be less of a "How to do it" than a "how not to do it", based on the premise that people need most support when things go wrong. By understanding how problems arise the process of recovery is made much easier. The book is structured around substantial sections, on a number of discrete themes, which may be read in isolation. For this reason, each chapter is provided with its own reference listing.

It is intended that the work should be self-contained, so that its essential messages can be appreciated without extensive further reading. The book, however, also provides a substantial bibliography, particularly of recent research findings, for those readers who wish to follow particular themes further.

In common with the majority of practitioners who are privileged to view the operations of a range of manufacturing companies, without the distraction of becoming involved in day-to-day problem solving (primarily consultants and academics), the author has encountered a number of generic industrial problems. Professional consultants make their living by developing standardized methodologies which are applicable to similar problems across a range of companies or industries. For the consultant the regular repetition of the same generic management deficiencies is the central prerequisite of profitability. From the alternative view of the academic, however, with a primary interest in education, there is often considerable frustration that the same mistakes are seen again and again.

Whilst the author approaches the current work from the viewpoint of the engineer, it is necessary to note that many of the attitudes prevalent among engineers are worthy of critical appraisal. There is no more ominous phrase in the engineering industry than ".. we like to think that we are the Rolls Royce of the left hand throttle widget industry ..". The speaker is usually totally insensitive to the fact that the Rolls Royce of the Aero Engine industry went comprehensively bankrupt, largely due to the same kind of complacent, technologically elitist disregard of basic industrial disciplines (see Wearne [10] and Heller [3]).

References

[1]   Kuba, Y., Master of Manufacturing Technology: the 70 Year History of MAZAK, N D Publications, Tokyo 1989.

[2]   Drucker, P. F., The New Realities, Heinemann, Oxford, England 1989.

[3]   Heller, R., The Naked Manager: Games Executives Play, Truman-Talley Dutton, New York 1985.

[4]   Crosby, P. B., Quality is Free, McGraw-Hill, New York 1979.

[5]   Porter, M. E., Competitive Advantage, Free Press, New York 1985.

[6]   Oakland, J. S., Total Quality Management, Heinemann, Oxford, England 1989.

[7]   Kanter, R. M., When Giants Learn to Dance: Mastering the Challenge of Strategy, Management and Careers in the 1990s, Simon and Schuster, London 1989.

[8]   Harvey-Jones, J., Making it Happen: Reflections on Leadership, Collins, London 1988.

[9]   Lynn, M., "Joker in the Pack (Trump: Surviving at the Top)", Business, November 1990, p181.

[10]   Wearne, S. H., A Review of Reports of Failures, Proceedings of the Institution of Mechanical Engineers, 1979, Volume 193, pp125-136.

Introduction

Aims and Objectives

Assumptions

Both the content and style of the current work have been designed with the intention of fulfilling a particular role in influencing the management of change in Manufacturing Systems. It is motivated by the belief that the problems are, to quote an old aphorism (used most recently by President Reagan) ".. simple – but not easy". Thus the reader may find some of the content trite or obvious. However the author makes no apology for this, believing that one of the major weapons of those who oppose change – those who will lose status, power or wealth, as a result of the change – is to exaggerate the difficulties and minimise the benefits of organizational change.

A second tenet of the current work is that Organizational Change requires the concentration of resources, expertise, authority and motivation, either in an individual or a group, as shown in Figure 1.1. Again, this may seem obvious, but may require radical rethinking of the fundamental objectives of the organization, in particular re-examination of the relationship between its primary functional groupings, particularly engineering, marketing, quality and, last but not least, finance. This might be taken to imply advocacy of the current trend towards modular, product-centred, business units, for which there are often good organizational pressures, but occasionally, more exceptionally, there may be equally good arguments for taking a diametrically opposite viewpoint. This is illustrated by Kanter [1] in justifying the adoption of functionally-based

Figure I-1. The Mechanism of Change

management by Apple Computers in 1983.

Management of change requires a number of stages for its successful implementation. Firstly, the need for change must be recognized. The appropriate strategies must then be identified. The mechanisms to enable the desired strategies must then be activated, often by removing inhibitions rather than introducing new ideas or methodologies. The plan must, finally, be viable, i.e. within the capability of the organization and compatible with market conditions.

Questions which are addressed include:

- The corporate culture, in particular its ability to respond to internal and external stimuli.

- The relationships between the management of the *Manufacturing Systems* and the overall *Corporate Strategy* of the enterprise.

- The *market position* of the enterprise and its own perception of the condition of the market.

- The position of *training* in the organization's Corporate Strategy.

- The management of *Information Technology* in the enterprise.

Whilst it is recognized that change can be impeded intentionally, e.g. for the reasons outlined above (anticipation of the loss of status, power or wealth), it is the contention of the current work that people are inhibited from initiating change largely because no one person, or group has the four prerequisites of knowledge, power, resources and motivation.

Market Awareness

There is a plethora of books on general management and a comparable number on the subject of the management of engineering operations. These will be referred to regularly in the text. In the current context, these correspond to the generic products in the marketplace. The classic texts on general management, by such authors as Drucker [2], McGregor [3], Burns and Stalker [4], and Woodward [5], remain as useful as when they were first published. Similar considerations apply to the literature on the management of engineering operations. Even despite the substantial effects of technological advances, particularly in the field of information technology, the underlying principles of production management and production technology remain substantively timeless. For example, the author still uses a second edition of the text by E. S. Buffa on Operations Management [6], although, at the last count, it has reached its eighth edition. Similar texts by Wild [7] and Hill [8] have also been used by the author. Other earlier works which are much less well-known cover subjects which preoccupy many managers currently. For example, Laird and Laird [9] address the issue of delegation in a style which is as topical now as it was then.

Equally influential, in the short term at least, are the inspirational texts epitomised by the work of Peters and Waterman [10]. As described by Kanter [1], these texts are, apparently, full of contradictions:

- Strategic needs versus the bottom line

- Entrepreneurial pressures versus fear of failure

- Excel in current activities versus devote more time to communication

- Attention to detail versus delegation

- Dedication to the mission versus flexibility, responsiveness etc.

- Emphatic leadership versus participation, consultation.

- Dedication to the job versus personal fitness

- "Succeed, succeed, succeed – and raise terrific children".

It would be easy to dismiss such exhortations if it were not for the fact that these paradoxes are all part of the management of change in Manufacturing Systems. Indeed, they are what makes it so much fun! Where the author feels obliged to express a (substantial) element of disquiet is the tendency for such texts to offer simplistic prescriptive solutions to extremely complex problems. To paraphrase H L Mencken: to every problem there is a solution which is simple, easily understood and completely wrong.

It is taken as a fundamental premise of the current work that people learn most from experience, particularly of an adverse nature. However, it would be totally impractical for people to rely solely on their own experience. Thus considerable weight is given in the current volume to the case study material and collations of key publications, for example Trevor [11], Gilder [12], Bignell et al. [13], Kanter [1] and Taylor and Harrison [14]. However, as will be seen, the conclusions reached in the current context will not necessarily coincide with those of the original analysts, since it is of interest to examine how many of these companies and individuals, which are subjects of the case studies, have not retained sustained benefits from the particular strategy which was the focus of the case study. Indeed, the award of the Guardian newspaper's "Young Businessman of the Year" has been singularly portentous of troubles ahead. As has been suggested, the text "Understanding Systems Failures", by Bignell and Fortune [15] is particularly relevant.

All of the above categories are generously provided for in the literature, and have provided source material for the present volume. However, the intention of this text is to present a balanced analysis of the problems of the management of change in Manufacturing Systems, which is accessible to all of the disciplinary groupings that constitute the enterprise.

This text is, therefore, intended to fit into a particular market niche. The fundamental objectives are to provide readers with the means to make sense of the pressures for change, and be equipped to identify how to gather their change prerequisites, i.e. knowledge, power, resources and motivation. By probing the relative strengths and weaknesses of the different participants in the management of Manufacturing Systems – the engineers, the accountants, the marketing specialists, the production operatives and others – the proponent of change may be able to marshall the change prerequisites to enable an individual or group to control the process of change.

References

[1]   Kanter, R. M., When Giants Learn to Dance: Mastering the Challenges of Strategy, Management and Careers in the 1990s, Simon and Schuster, New York 1989.

[2]   Drucker, P. F., The Practice of Management, Heinemann, London 1955.

[3]   McGregor, D., The Human Side of Enterprise, McGraw-Hill, New York 1960.

[4]   Burns, T. and Stalker, G., The Management of Innovation, Tavistock, London 1961.

[5]   Woodward, J., Industrial Organization: Theory and Practice, Oxford University Press, Oxford 1965.

[6]   Buffa, E. S., Modern Production Management, Second Edition, John Wiley, New York 1965

[7]   Wild, R., Production and Operations Management, 4th Edition, Cassell Educational, London 1989.

[8]   Hill, T., Production/Operations Management, Prentice-Hall, New Jersey 1983.

[9]   Laird, D. A. and Laird, E. C., The Techniques of Delegating: How to Get Things Done through Others, McGraw-Hill, New York 1957.

[10] Peters, T. J. and Waterman R. H. Jnr., In Search of Excellence, Harper and Row, New York 1982.

[11] Trevor, M., Toshiba's New British Company: Competitiveness through Innovation in Industry, Policy Studies Institute, London 1988.

[12] Gilder, G., The $pirit of Enterprise, Simon and Schuster, New York 1984.

[13] Bignell V. et al. (Editors), Manufacturing Systems: Context, Applications and Techniques, Open University/ Blackwell, Oxford, England 1985.

[14] Taylor B. and Harrison, J., The Manager's Casebook of Business Strategy, Heinemann, London 1990.

[15] Bignell V. and Fortune, J., Understanding Systems Failures, Manchester University Press/ Open University, Manchester, England 1984.

N.B. In the current context early editions have been cited, where appropriate; several of the texts mentioned here have later editions.

Context

It is, perhaps, worthwhile initially to specify what is meant by the expression "Manufacturing Systems", even what is meant by "Systems". For many, this would seem unnecessarily abstruse or pedantic. However, misunderstandings can easily occur where readers from different backgrounds have different perceptions of the meanings of even basic concepts. This is compounded by the proliferation of acronyms, often referred to as "Alphabet Soup" which may have completely different significance even in closely related contexts. For example, to a Production Manager CAPM means "Computer-Aided Production Management", whereas a Financial Controller might assume a reference to the "Capital Asset Pricing Model", which is used to evaluate risk in Portfolio Analysis. Similarly, CAPP may mean "Computer-Aided Part Programming" to the Production Technologist, whereas to a colleague in Production Management it is more likely to mean "Computer-Aided Process Planning".

Although the definition may appear rather abstract, a System may be defined as a collection of objects or entities whose relationships are in some way directed. Anything not an element of the system is part of its *environment*. The system is separated from its environment by its *boundary* which implies the existence of input-output relationships. The successful management of change in Manufacturing Systems requires flexibility in the definition of these boundaries. Traditional conceptions of Manufacturing Systems are probably far too restrictive in the current context, being limited to the analysis of Production Technology and Production Management. It is necessary, therefore, to include, *within the system boundary*, a much wider variety of system entities and relationships including, for example, cultural, financial and economic factors. Increasingly, importance must also be accorded to the ecological impact, both of the manufacturing processes and the resulting product.

Both within the system itself, and between elements of the system and its environment, the relationships are often characterized by their degree of coupling. Two or more elements which depend directly on each other for control of their actions are described as *closely coupled*. Elements which provide information or advice to each other are described as *loosely coupled*. Elements which have no formal relationships are described as *uncoupled* or *de-coupled*.

Figures I.2 and I.3 show alternative viewpoints of two systems, each corresponding to the organization of a business unit. In each case the traditional hierarchical model is shown with a corresponding system model, illustrating the structural differences in system control. In the generic line-staff model (see Woodward [1] p105), the first case, Figure I.2, based on a traditional functional hierarchy, the four change prerequisites, expertise, resources, authority and motivation, are insufficiently represented within the system boundary for the system to change independently of the corporate strategy, since the indigenous management rely on authorization of their proposed actions by the executive. Essential staff within the business unit are likely to spend a disproportionate amount of their time reporting to the corporate headquarters, seeking the essential resources and authority to carry out their work. This interaction may dissipate unnecessary energy, distract management from pressing internal priorities and make them less accessible to their subordinates. When represented in systems terms, the input-output relationships are strongly executive, with internal actions dependent on external approval. A complementary consequence is that headquarters staff, whose primary role should be the development and implementation of the corporate strategy, are liable also to dissipate their skills, time and energy in meddling in decisions which could quite well be devolved to business unit

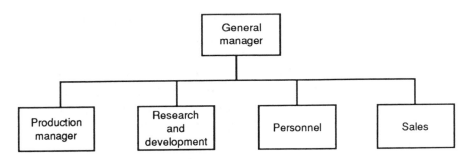

Figure I-2. Functional Organization

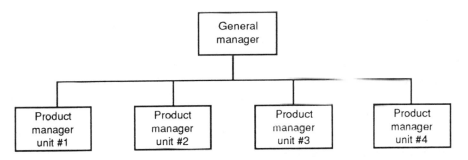

Figure I-3. Product-centred Organization (after Woodward [1] p105 and p102)

level. (See Harvey-Jones [2]).

In the second case, shown in Figure I.3, (based on Woodward [1] p102) authority has been devolved to autonomous business units, together with the control of sufficient resources to enable change. Examining the system formalism, input-output relationships now primarily entail communication rather than control. The corporate centre provides services and guidance rather than interventional control. Figure I.4 contrasts these differing properties of communications in product-centred and functional organizations.

Organizational structure patterns have become significantly

more complex than the hierarchies described by Woodward. Goold [3] analyzes a substantial proportion of Britain's leading companies (and some overseas examples), examining their organizational structure in some detail. A more realistic viewpoint recognizes that the scheme of connectivity between employees varies according to the particular managerial task under consideration. Figure I.5 shows how different connections between the same employees can result from various aspects of their jobs.

It would be wrong to suggest that interventionist management behaviour corresponds directly to functional organization or, conversely, that autonomous, product-centred, business-unit based hierarchies are perfectly correlated with healthy manufacturing systems. Indeed, the appropriateness of each, in any given context, is a function of a wide range of variables, including, for example, size of the enterprise, characteristics of the products, distribution of the company's manufacturing plants, and their geographical relationship to their markets.

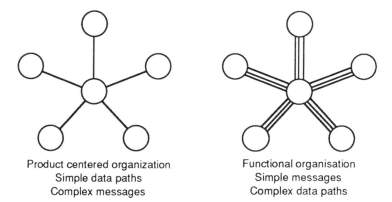

Product centered organization
Simple data paths
Complex messages

Functional organisation
Simple messages
Complex data paths

Figure I-4. Message Complexity in Different Organizational Structures

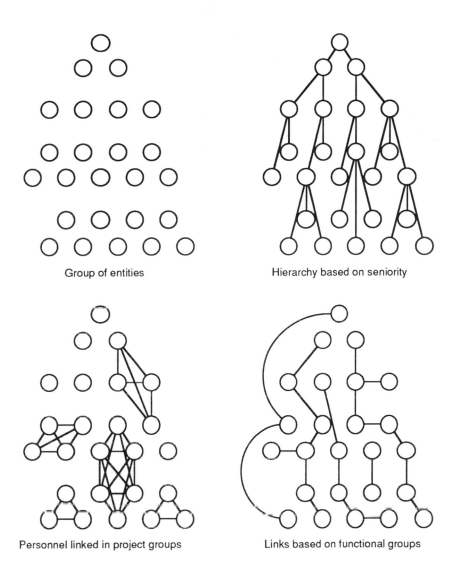

Group of entities

Hierarchy based on seniority

Personnel linked in project groups

Links based on functional groups

Figure I-5. Multiple Views of System Connectivity

References

[1] Woodward, J., *Industrial Organization: Theory and Practice*, 2nd Edn. Oxford University Press, England 1980.

[2] Harvey-Jones, J., *Making it Happen: Reflections on Leadership*, Collins, London 1988.

[3] Goold M. (with Quinn, J. J.), *Strategic Control: Milestones for Long-term Performance*, The Economist Books/Hutchinson, London, 1990.

1

The Practice of Management

Checklists for Good Management

Some of the most popular texts for managers are nothing more than a set of checklists. There is little doubt that adherence to, and regular maintenance of, checklists of routine activities should become second nature to managers of manufacturing systems in their steady state. What is more questionable, however, is whether or not it is possible to devise standardized behaviour patterns under conditions of radical change. In the current context three sources will be discussed, each of which the author has found of substantial value, both in teaching and industrial collaboration.

The Technically Progressive Firm

Recent research has demonstrated that successful manufacturing organizations demonstrate the overwhelming majority of the following characteristics:

- High quality of incoming communications.
- A deliberate survey of potential ideas.
- A willingness to share knowledge.
- A willingness to take new knowledge on licence and to enter joint ventures.
- A readiness to look outside the firm (for new ideas).

- Effective internal communication and co-ordination.
- High status of science and technology in the firm.
- A consciousness of costs and profits in the research and development departments (if any).
- Rapid replacement of machines.
- A sound policy of recruitment for management.
- An ability to attract talented people.
- A willingness to arrange for the effective training of staff.
- Use of management techniques.
- Identifying the outcome of investment decisions.
- High quality in the chief executive(s).
- Adequate provision for intermediate managers.
- Good quality in intermediate management.
- An ability to bring the best out of managers.
- Use of scientists and technologists on the Board of Directors.
- A readiness to look ahead.
- A high rate of expansion.
- Ingenuity in getting round material and equipment shortages.
- An effective selling policy.
- Good technical service to customers.

The statement at the beginning of the chapter was true: recent research *has* confirmed that these factors are important in the success of manufacturing enterprises. Indeed, the list could quite easily be mistaken for a description of 'Japanese' manufacturing success recipes. *However*, this particular list was derived from a survey of best practice carried out in the UK in the mid 1950s (Carter and Williams [1]).

Criteria for Survival

Michael Jordan is a name that few British managers should wish to hear in a professional capacity. As one of the senior partners of Cork Gully, the insolvency practitioners, he has presided over rather too many company receiverships. His indicators of company ill-health were compiled some years before the rash of corporate failures in the late 1980s in companies which had presented sets of (apparently) healthy audited accounts shortly before their demise. Jordan attacked this problem in particular in his discussion [2]. He suggests that the warning signs in a number of business failures were apparent and that '..it's the failure to spot the warning signs that's the real worry.'

Jordan's warning signs are summarized here because they are likely to prejudice the process of change in manufacturing systems, rather than lead to the immediate demise of the company.

Management defects which lead to failure:

'... an autocratic chief executive ...
... a policy for all out growth ...
... a lack of financial skills on the board ...
... an imbalance of skills on the board ...
... a lack of management skills below board level ...
... poor budgetary control ...
... inadequate cash flow planning ...
... poorly maintained costing systems ...
... the inclination of management to window dress its accounts by such means as leasing equipment rather than purchasing it ...
... failure to respond to changing circumstances ... '. -

The last of these indicators Jordan considers the most significant. He subdivides this category:

'.. Old attitudes towards employees;

out of date products;

obsolete plant and equipment;

out-of-date marketing;

an ageing board of directors;

no computers.'

Jordan's financial indicators are also relevant, but will be discussed when financial aspects of change in manufacturing systems are described. It can be seen that there are conflicts between the two lists given by Carter and Williams, and Jordan. In particular, Jordan views rapid expansion as a potential danger sign whereas Carter and Williams regarded it as indicative of good management.

The Techniques of Delegating

In the study by Carter and Williams a number of issues which are still topical in the 1990s are discussed. What is of interest here is that although their arguments are as carefully presented as in more recent work – perhaps more so – their conclusions are often diametrically opposed. For example they recognize problems of communication in hierarchical organizations. Whereas the consensus among more recent authors has been to broaden the hierarchy, both increasing the span of control and reducing the number of layers, Carter and Williams recommended narrowing the hierarchy to focus the managerial effort on a narrower range of activities. This conclusion was, however, in contrast to the contemporary views of Drucker [3] whose views are as fresh today as they were then:

'One telling symptom of malorganisation is the growth of levels of management – bespeaking poor or confused objectives, failure to remove poor performers, over-centralisation or lack of proper activities analysis.' (Ibid. pp196-7.)

Where many of the more recent texts are deficient is in the necessary detail which will enable the orderly planning of the implementation of their prescriptive solutions. Indeed, what many authors appear to advocate is the wholesale elimination of whole layers of hierarchy, relying on the inherent robustness of the organization to adapt to the new circumstances. This philosophy probably dates from the prescriptive approach pioneered in 'Up The Organization' by Townsend [4].

A more considered approach, more in sympathy with the views of this author, is the work on the techniques of delegating by Laird and Laird [5]. As with the overwhelming majority of management principles, the care of preparation and sincerity of execution of any strategic plan are perhaps more important than the absolute quality of the proposed solution. Certainly an otherwise perfect solution can be destroyed by poor implementation. Furthermore, both successful and unsuccessful management actions tend to be self-reinforcing and, ultimately, self-perpetuating.

The checklist of guidelines which precedes Laird and Laird's chapter 11 (in common with each of the other chapters) is reproduced here:

'Delegate experience and variety

Delegate 'wholeness' and clear objectives

Delegate for interest and willingness

Delegate enough challenge, but not too much

Delegate a success sequence

Delegate in a climate of mutual trust'

If a company's management gets these basics right then the natural characteristics of the business are likely to become self-evident. There is no one right answer as to the correct organizational structure of an enterprise. It depends on company history, markets, the nature of the manufacturing processes and many other variables.

References

[1]   Carter, C. F. and Williams, B. R., *Industry and Technical Progress: Factors Governing the Speed and Application of Science*, Oxford University Press, England, 1957.
[2]   Jordan, M., *Criteria for Survival*, Cork Gully, Unpublished/Undated presentation.
[3]   Drucker, P. F., *The Practice of Management*, Mercury, London, 1955.
[4]   Townsend, R., *Up The Organization*, Michael Joseph, New York, 1970.
[5]   Laird D. A. and Laird, E. C., *The Techniques of Delegating*, McGraw-Hill, New York, 1957.

2

System Modelling

Some Basic System Concepts

In recent years the terminology of systems theory has become so generally pervasive that it is often assumed that a listener will automatically derive understanding of the ideas expressed by a speaker, based on a common reservoir of basic concepts. Unfortunately, however, such an assumption is often unjustified, as the widespread, and often indiscriminate, use of system jargon may lead to the vocabulary being absorbed subliminally in isolation from its meaning.

System theory derives from a range of different disciplines including, but not restricted to, topology, electronics, control theory, computer science and psychology.

A system comprises a *set of entities* whose behaviour is in some way dependent. External to the system is its *environment*. Systems are designed or analyzed by means of a system *model*, which is an abstract representation (often grossly simplified) of the real system.

Graphical Representations

The most pervasive visualization of a system is in terms of its graph, in which the entities of the system are represented by nodes and their dependencies are depicted by arcs, as shown in Figure 2-1. The most rudimentary graph is the *simple graph*,

7

where no significance is attributable to the arcs. Where a dependency is of a <from> <to> form it is important to express some degree of precedence, for example either in terms of time or seniority. In this case a *directed graph* is used. The graphs used in project planning, Critical Path Planning and PERT, for example, are directed graphs, with the direction indicating sequential dependence of planned activities. Where the nature of the dependency between entities is explicitly defined the system representation is described as an *attributed graph*. The elements identified in a 'broad brush' analysis of the system are often non-trivial systems in their own right, usually called *sub-systems*, and the progressive refinement of the detail of this graph leads to the concept of a *recursive graph*, where the elements of the system are themselves systems of significant complexity. When the system has been reduced to a level where elements have minimal internal complexity, the resulting elements are described as *system primitives*.

To illustrate this rationale, it is worth considering some examples:

SYSTEM	SUB-SYSTEM	SYSTEM PRIMITIVE
Customer-deliverable product	Sub-assemblies	Individual components
Company workforce	Department	Individual employees
Flexible manufacturing system	Manufacturing cell	Machine tool

The structure of a system is often described as its *Topology*. Certain generic categories of topology have special significance, for example when a graph has no loops it is described as a *tree*. Consistent with the metaphor, sub-systems are often described as branches and primitives as leaves. Trees are widely used as

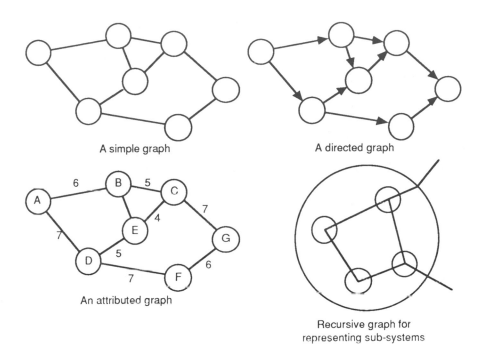

Figure 2-1. Graphical Representations

system representations, often inappropriately, for example (as will be seen) the ubiquitous hierarchical model to describe management control in organizations.

Metaphors for System Topology and Attribution

Many of the current metaphors of system theory derive from the closely related disciplines of electrical circuit theory, control systems design and computer network design. These concepts will be used here to form a basis for understanding the design issues for management of change in manufacturing systems. The justification for such an approach stems from the contrast between the ways in which the analysis of engineering and management systems have been undertaken. Whereas system representations in the technical domain are necessarily well developed and unambiguous because of the need for predictable, accurate and reliable performance to specification, those in the management domain are subjective, limited in scope and ambiguous. Nevertheless there are sufficient similarities between technological and management systems for models from the former to provide powerful metaphors for the analysis of the latter.

Even in the relatively well-defined technological domain, standards for linking system elements have encountered substantial resistance, largely due to the vested interests of the competing companies. For example the general standard for networking, the Open System Interconnection (OSI) model [1], remains the subject of partisan rivalry in the computer industry. Two substantial groups have formed (the Open Software Foundation containing DEC, Hewlett Packard, IBM and Philips, and the Unix International group containing Amdahl, Control Data, Sun and Unisys) each committed to a different version of AT&T's UNIX operating system (Schofield [2]). A third group retains membership of both organizations.

Unfortunately, as with other standards, much of the literature concerning OSI is couched in impenetrable jargon, likely to appeal only to the most ardent of pedants. The most accessible account known to the author was published in a relatively obscure publication, by Beeston [3], but deserves a wider audience. The standard defines seven 'layers' corresponding to progressive tranformation between user requirements and network processes. Beeston decribes the function of the standard in the following terms:

> 'A simple analogy is with the postal service. Layers 1 to 4
> are effectively the equivalent of the postal transport service

for controlling and routing the letter once it has been posted. All the user has to do is correctly define the address on the envelope. The user is not concerned with the means of delivery or routing at all. Certainly the address has to be correct, although the degree of standardization is very high internationally and the system can cope surprisingly well with quite large errors or omissions.

'The upper layers, 5 to 7, are concerned, in postal terms, with the contents of the envelope. Layer 5 is concerned with a session of several messages, layer 6 the presentation, i.e. the script and language of the letter, and layer 7 is the application.'

Based on the ideas of the Open System Interconnection model, General Motors developed the Manufacturing Automation Protocol (General Motors [4]). In his address to the 1984 automotive forum in Michigan, Roger Smith, then Chairman of General Motors, described the problem in the following terms:

'We are limited in the manufacturing efficiency we can achieve by the Tower of Babel that exists among robots and other computer-aided programmable devices. Only about 15 per cent of the 40,000 programmable devices in GM plants now can communicate outside their own processes. That's because each uses vendor-unique communications methods. It's as if each of these machines were speaking its own language – French, Italian, Russian, Chinese, Hungarian or whatever. They need an interpreter. And that interpreter comes in the very costly form of custom hardware and custom software needed to interface between different processes.'[5]

Thus the development of MAP was driven by an urgent industrial need, by a company with sufficient leverage to ensure that its views were heard in the marketplace. The company insisted that all relevant equipment procured by the company conform to the standard since October 1982.

Complementary to MAP is TOP: the Technical Office Protocol. Whereas MAP is primarily concerned with Computer-Aided Manufacture, TOP controls information exchange in the design environment. The links between OSI, MAP and TOP, and their place within Computer-Integrated Manufacture (CIM) are described in a number of sources, see for example [6].

The nature of the dependency between two elements of a system depends partially on the inherent nature of the two entities but is also the outcome of both explicit and implicit managerial decisions.

Perhaps the most important issue in the design of any system is its basic topology. As has been suggested, existing models from technological system design are of substantial value in the construction of suitable models either for constructing new management systems or analysis (and improvement) of existing managerial structures.

There are three basic topological structures used in computer networking: bus, ring and star (see Figure 2-2). Each has its own particular strengths and weaknesses. Consequently, these different structures are often combined in more complex systems. Similar structures are identifiable in managerial control systems, although these are often the result of evolutionary processes, rather than designed for purpose, and may no longer be appropriate for long-term survival of the organization.

The most powerful structure, in terms of speed of response, for manufacturing system control is the *bus* topology. In addition to its role of connection of computers externally, it is the means whereby microcomputers communicate internally. When used to connect computers externally, all nodes are connected by means of a single open-ended cable.

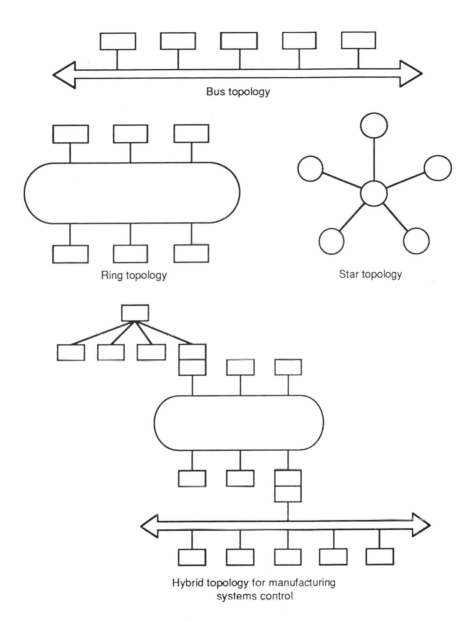

Figure 2-2. Topological Structures

In the *star* structure all communications are routed through a central node. Historically this usually entailed an interventional role, with control of the content and availability of the data to other nodes in the network. Latterly the central node has often taken the role of a *file server*, much more limited in its powers of intervention, with a primary role of ensuring orderly flow of information in the system. Since topology concerns relational connectivity rather than spatial proximity the ubiquitous management hierarchy model can be constructed using linked stars.

The third common topology for a network is the *ring*, widely used for the management of *Local Area Networks (LANs)*. Analogous with an airport baggage carousel, messages circulate around a closed loop, being placed or taken off by connected nodes. Consistent with this analogy, the messages circulate around the ring in *packets* of data.

Key issues for the management of information in networks are the precedence relationships between devices, the methods of gaining the attention of the target device and access conventions. The most common precedence relationship is the master-slave pair, where the subservient device acts under the control of its superior. In other networks each device has equal status and competes for access to the network, *access by contention*. The *ethernet* system (developed by Xerox) uses a modified access by contention (Carrier Sense Multiple Access with Collision Detection – CSMA/CD) where devices attempt to anticipate possible congestion by listening for potential collisions of data packets prior to placing their own messages on the ring. The alternative IBM Token Ring Network uses an *access by permission* convention. Like William Golding's Lord of the Flies, where possession of the conch shell gave the right to speak, access to the network is allowed only to devices in possession of a token, which circulates the network. Such networks are commonly described as *loosely coupled* systems. In contrast, most star networks are *closely coupled* systems.

Access conventions are dependent largely on the perceived urgency of typical messages. Where messages are generally of a routine nature the most likely default access strategy is that of device *polling*. In this mode the controller will regularly interrogate other devices on the network asking for current status information. This involves the controller devoting a substantial proportion of its working time soliciting reports which are often of a routine nature. In systems where the prevailing decision-making environment is consistent with *management by exception*, i.e. the target device only needs a report if a fault condition is detected, then access using *interrupts* is feasible. In this case the reporting device is given access to one of the target device's input ports. Usually the input port is partitioned and each part is assigned a different level of priority to enable the target device to judge the urgency of the interrupt, from passing relatively routine information to warnings of imminent catastrophic failure. In systems where speed of response is of the highest priority, for example safety-critical systems, then *direct memory access (DMA)* would be allowed. This allows the sender to gain direct access into the memory of the recipient. Obviously such a strategy must be the exception rather than the rule and this level of privilege only allowed for a restricted class of senders under strongly controlled conditions.

As has been suggested, each of the different network topologies has its strengths and weaknesses. Consequently, large-scale manufacturing systems often comprise a linked graph containing each of the topologies described above. Different local area networks are linked through *bridges* and connections to wide area networks are achieved using *gateways*.

Choice of Topology and Networking Protocol

In assessing the suitability of a particular topology for a proposed network there are a number of factors which should be taken into consideration. These include:

- volume of data
- variety of data
- value of information
- data integrity
- urgency
- access to data (security vs availability)

In devising computer communication methodologies a crucial consideration is the choice of protocol. This entails specification both of the general principles and also the detail of the transfer of information between devices. As described by Street [7] OSI forms a general framework for specifying network protocols rather than a network protocol in itself. This is particularly important since many of the most common interfacing standards were originally based on proprietary products, examples being the IEEE 488 standard, based on Hewlett Packard's GPIB bus, and the standard parallel printer bus, which is still universally referred to as the Centronics interface despite its general standardization.

Even where standards are applied, there is often a large (often intolerably so) amount of discretion left to the user. The most notorious example of this is probably the RS232 interface bus which is in widespread use for interfacing a wide variety of computers and process equipment, including numerically-controlled machine tools. The standard allows a wide degree of discretion to the user, in terms of the speed of data transmission, the number of data and control lines, and the physical connection media. This uncertainty is often compounded by the failure of the equipment manufacturers to observe the few constraints which the standard does impose.

The linking of computer hardware requires physical connection of two or more devices. Complexity of the physical connection depends to a significant extent on the choice between serial or parallel connection, as shown in Figure 2.3. With parallel communication complex data streams can be transmitted at high speeds. Because data is transmitted synchronously through a number of lines, such connections are commonly more susceptible to corruption than in serial transmission. In conseqence, parallel data transmission is restricted to devices which are short distances apart, for example the IEEE 488 bus will only tolerate distances of a few metres between devices.

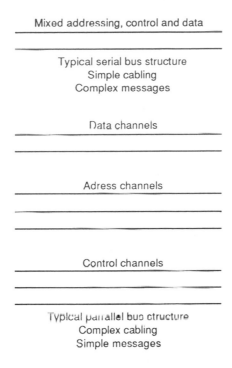

Mixed addressing, control and data

Typical serial bus structure
Simple cabling
Complex messages

Data channels

Adress channels

Control channels

Typical parallel bus structure
Complex cabling
Simple messages

Figure 2-3. Comparison of Bus Structures

Alternative Topologies

As has been described, communication links in complex manufacturing systems are often constructed using all three of the structures defined above. This will be referred to as a hybrid network.

A particular form of hybrid network is that of the *matrix organization*, shown in Figure 2.4, which is regarded as particularly appropriate in manufacturing organizations (see Brearley [8]), although it has been comprehensively challenged by Harvey-Jones [9]. The matrix organization may, however, be regarded as the superimposing of a network of project management on top of a functional network, and thus is a special case of a more general topological model commonly encountered in systems design. Consequently, extending this analysis, and again taking a metaphor from electronic circuit design, the multi-layer circuit board, different managerial models may be superposed on a common set of entities with each layer having a different connection network.

As has been suggested previously, the topologies described earlier are ideal for well-structured problems where standardized design methodologies can be employed. For poorly structured problems these approaches can be of considerable value in the qualitative visualization of the behaviour of the system, but can be extremely dangerous for quantitative analysis of system behaviour, in particular predictive modelling. A relatively recent development has been the idea of *neural networks*, which are based on the operation of neural connections in living organisms. In many respects these models are much more representative of the connectivity generally found in the management of industrial organizations, in particular those of manufacturing systems. Neural modelling methodologies are very much in their infancy but, in the long term, are extremely promising for analysis of management systems.

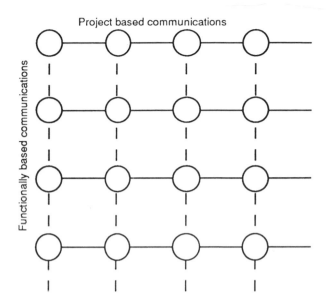

Figure 2-4. Matrix Organization for Project-Based Environments

The neural network comprises a number of *layers*, with each node connected to its neighbours in the layers above and below, as shown in Figure 2.5. Whereas in the topologies described previously the connectivity was (intentionally) restricted, in a non-trivial neural network (i.e. with a number of intermediate layers) there are numerous information paths linking the source and the target of a message. As with physical neurons, the communication and control systems in the management of manufacturing systems adapt to usage patterns. The more often a link is utilized the more easy it is for that data path to be used again, much as the flow of water along a stream reinforces the path of the water course. It can be seen that neural networks are likely to be of increasing importance in the modelling of management systems as the relevant theory is developed.

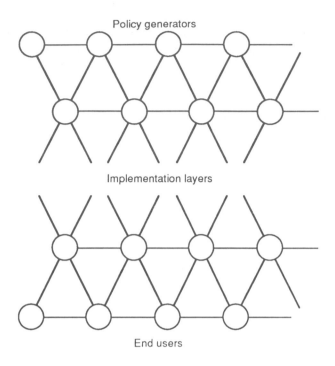

Figure 2-5. Modelling Industrial Systems Using Neural Nets

References

[1] *ISO International Standard 7498, Information Processing Systems – Open Systems Inter-connection – Basic Reference Model*, International Organization for Standardization, Geneva, 1983

[2] Schofield, J., "Open warfare: Who owns the UNIX standard and how will it develop?" *Open Systems Computing*, 1990, 1(4), pp37-8.

[3] Beeston, J. W., "Industrial communications – an overview", in *Planning for Automated Manufacture*, Institution of Mechanical Engineers Conference Publication 1986-10, 1986, Bury St Edmunds, England, pp97-104.

[4] General Motors Corporation, *Manufacturing Automation Protocol – Version 3.0 Implementation Release*, 1987.

[5] "Communications-Friendly Machines are Needed on our Factory Floors", in *Mechanical Engineering*, June 1985, pp34-39.

[6] Department of Trade and Industry, *Through MAP and TOP to CIM*, HMSO, London, 1988.

[7] Street, Y., "Conversing computers", *Professional Engineering*, January 1989, pp37-39.

[8] Brearley, A., "Design Management", in *The Gower Handbook of Management*, Editors D Lock and N Farrow, Gower, London, 1988, pp404-444.

[9] Harvey-Jones, J., *Making it Happen: Reflections on Leadership*, Collins, London, 1988, p213

3

Technical Change and Corporate Culture

The Nature of Technical Change

Daniel and Millward [1] defined three forms of technical change:

- Advanced Technical Change: introduction of new plant, machinery or equipment, that includes the new microelectronics technology .....

- Conventional Technical Change: new plant, machinery or equipment not incorporating microelectronics ....

- Organizational Change: substantial changes in work organization or working practices not involving new plant, machinery or equipment.

Whilst these divisions may seem logical to the reader who is not technologically trained, they are of less value when viewed from an engineering standpoint. In particular, microelectronics technology may be used either to replace existing machine functions with equivalent emulations or to provide the machine with a function, or group of functions which were not previously available. For example, designs generated on state-of-the-art CAD (Computer-Aided Design) systems are still commonly transformed, within the CAM (Computer-Aided Manufacture) functions, into a standardized machine language designed in the

1950s (Manual Part Programming Language – MPPL). Subsequently newer, more sophisticated languages, such as APT (Automatically Programmed Tools) have had to be provided with post-processor utilities to convert their output into MPPL. This is due, at least in part, to the fact that there is a substantial installed base of machine controllers which can only utilize the earlier language. This is a self-reinforcing process, since new machines have had to be designed to process this anachronistic language, to ensure compatiblility with other machines installed previously. It is a recurring theme of the current work that a sequence of rationally based, logical steps can lead to an illogical and irrational, and hence unstable, end result.

The key categories of change in the present context are simpler than those defined by Daniel and Millward [1]. Indeed it is a central tenet of the current work that substantive changes in the organization of manufacturing systems are likely to necessitate a combination of the three classes of change defined by Daniel and Millward. Change will be defined here, rather simplistically, either as incremental or radical. The more consistently successful types of enterprises, at least within recent history, have been the companies which have, perhaps unwittingly, espoused the Japanese principle of *Kaizen* – based on institutionalized incremental change. For example, Imai [2], makes an explicit contrast between Kaizen and innovation in the following terms:

'Western management worships at the altar of innovation. ... Innovation is dramatic, a real attention getter. Kaizen, on the other hand, is often undramatic and subtle, and its results are seldom immediately visible. While Kaizen is a continuous process, innovation is generally a one-shot phenomenon.'

(Imai [2] p23.)

At the other extreme, Foster [3] argues that enterprises should constantly be seeking opportunities for innovation because incremental change is, from his viewpoint, a self-limiting process.

It should be recognized that neither philosophy need be followed to the exclusion of the other. Indeed, whenever one or the other dominates the corporate behaviour of an enterprise, one of the key responsibilities of those charged with corporate strategy is to maintain the possible benefits of the alternative approach under constant review.

The Need for Change

Change stimuli are commonly classified into internal or external processes. In the former category are included both technological and managerial advances. Technological aspects include, for example, the availability of new manufacturing processes, machinery, materials and production methods. Managerial influences encompass the structure of the organization itself, the control and communication structures, and the skills and attitudes of the workforce. External factors include market conditions, economic trends and legislative actions.

Generic Problems

A central paradox of industrial management is that substantial numbers of companies appear to remain financially viable in spite of severe limitations in their operating systems and product portfolios. A substantial proportion of companies retain their competitiveness not through their own efforts, but by the inadequacies of their competitors.

Thus, at any one time, there are substantial numbers of companies which are "accidents waiting to happen". At the time of writing, there are several topical cases. For example, there was an acrimonious dispute between senior staff at the insolvent Atlantic Computers and those at their parent company, British and Commonwealth, as to the exact date when the financial difficulties of the subsidiary were reported to the parent company. Whatever the truth of this controversy, the fact remains that there are several important lessons which are relevant to the current work: firstly, the sale of computers was only one relatively minor facet of the business of the company, which was primarily a financial services operation; secondly, the profitability of the business was largely dependent on the present value of the (notoriously unreliable) projected residual value of the computers traded by the company. Both of these aspects are of considerable importance in the management of change in manufacturing systems. Other industrial case studies will be discussed at appropriate points in the text.

Manufacturing systems operate in a dynamic environment and, consequently, are subject to evolutionary processes. As with all such processes, advantage is gained by adapting to the ambient conditions prevailing in the system's environment. By a process of incremental change, each system responds to the changes in its environment and becomes comparatively more competitive. However the system now contains the seeds of its own destruction since in the long term, as the system becomes increasingly more specialized, it becomes more vulnerable to environmental perturbations.

The historical development of manufacturing systems reflects this developmental model. The overwhelming majority of existing manufacturing systems originated in small-scale jobbing operations. Where repeated orders were received subsequently, batching of the jobs was seen as an advantageous procedure. Expansion of demand led to the perception that further economies of scale depended on changes in manufacturing systems design, from process- to product-dominant factory organization (Gallagher [4]). What was not recognized for many years was that the acceptance of this evolutionary process prevented the perception that the advantages of the application of the methods of mass production to the problem of batch production could provide major economies of scale. Thus the development of Group Technology described by Mitrofanov, in Russia, did not originate in an environment where significant evolutionary processes had taken place, but rather where industrial production methods had been transplanted in their entirety. Group Technology was applied, and advanced, in the United Kingdom at an early stage but was undermined by lack of understanding of the organizational prerequisites for successful implementation, and gained an undeserved reputation for fallibility, largely because of its application to inappropriate manufacturing systems.

As has been mentioned, one of the more remarkable features of Manufacturing Systems is their tolerance of inefficiencies. This is particularly pertinent to the subject of the financial control of manufacturing organizations. A persuasive theme in much of the recent management literature is that a substantial number of manufacturing companies:

- Have only a general idea as to the overall profitability of the business

- Are likely to have a misleading view of the historical, contemporary and future contributions of individual business units to the viability of the group

- Are likely to have no information whatsoever about the profitability of individual products, or groups of products, in a form compatible with other financial information.

The relationship, and in particular the compatibility, between different financial measurement methodologies in manufacturing companies has been addressed, with some eloquence, by Johnson and Kaplan [5]. Perpetuation of the inefficiencies in the financial control systems of companies is, perhaps, rather puzzling in the light of the sophisticated computer-based packages now widely available. Whilst the author finds many of the populist management literature confusing and contradictory, John Naisbitt [6] explained this precisely as '..drowning in information but starved of knowledge'.

Cultural Considerations

In parallel with developments in production technology, production management methods evolved with a substantial dependency on the technology. Since the technology of mass production was perceived as specialized, job functions were simplified and authoritarian methods of management prevailed, typified by the work of F W Taylor and his associates, in particular those described as "Scientific Management". L P Alford defined four 'Laws of Manufacturing Management' (see Jaffe [7]):

1. Law of specialization: (specialization of the job) reducing the number of the mental or manual operations for each job improves quality and increases output.

2. Law of division of effort: (specialization of the individual) assignment of very few mental or manual tasks that the worker is particularly adapted to perform improves quality and increases output.
   (This implies that as responsibility is narrowed efficiency is improved.)

3. Law of transfer of skill: (specialization of tools and machines) the skill and attention a tool or machine requires is inverse to the skill transferred to the

mechanism.

4.   Law of Simplification: restricting the range to a single product or a few types or sizes tends to improve quality and lower production costs.

Whilst this set of criteria apparently provides a reasonable response to the problems of management strategy in mass production, uncritical application of this type of approach leads to divisive and confrontational personnel relations attitudes in other categories of manufacturing systems. McGregor [8] termed this philosophy 'Theory X', which bases management strategy on the view that the workforce has no intrinsic motivation and hence cannot be trusted to work autonomously. Such a viewpoint is self-reinforcing and self-perpetuating. McGregor's alternative style of management, termed 'Theory Y', assumes that people are naturally innovative and that the role of management is to enable the success of the inherent will of the individual members of the workforce.

Whereas McGregor's theories largely apply to the worker as an individual, Ouchi's 'Theory Z' [9] recognizes that the behaviour of a group is not necessarily the direct summation of that of its individuals. The three key elements of Theory Z are:

• a collective work ethic;

• loyalty to fellow workers; and

• trust between individuals.

Espousal of this philosophy is claimed to be a suitable basis for improved teamwork, communication and shared goals. This strategy provides the stereotype for the "Japanese" management philosophy. A key question is whether such methodologies can be introduced across cultural boundaries.

There are numerous instances of management theories which have been developed in one culture, either national or corporate, but have not flourished, which have subsequently been adopted with considerable success within other nations or enterprises. A typical case being the methods of W Edwards Deming. Tribus [10] describes the comparative acceptance of Deming's theories in the following way:

> 'The Japanese revere the man who taught them that higher quality means lower cost. But in his own country, W Edwards Deming has found few who will listen.'

As will be seen, the Japanese have adapted Deming's philosophy to match their own cultural heritage. Perhaps the most interesting description being that by Ishikawa [11].

These management philosophies will be considered again in more detail later in the text.

Pressures for Change and Change Agents

As has already been described, for the cases of production costing (Johnson and Kaplan [5] and Group Technology Burbidge [12]), system evolution may lead incrementally, and logically, to a position of meta-stable equilibrium, (i.e. although the current system state is stable, and optimised locally, given the progression of earlier states, a far more advantageous state could be achieved by re-solving the problem from first principles). Consequently, many Manufacturing Systems are capable of absorption, and resistance, of a huge amount of the pressure for change. In such circumstances, a consensus may emerge that militates against creativity in system design. Although staff may be aware of the deficiencies of the system, they become resigned to the acceptance of these limitations because of the perception that the improvements desired can only be realized at an unacceptable cost.

An example of the contrasts between incremental and radical change is given by Shingo [13]. In 1970 Toyota Motor Company found that exchange of dies in their 1000 tonne stamping machine took four hours, whereas Volkswagen achieved exchange in two. After some six months' intensive effort, Shingo had managed to reduce the Toyota exchange time to one and a half hours, by following a systematic incremental approach.

It was a source of considerable concern, therefore, when Shingo found, some three months later, that Taiichi Ohno, the Senior Managing Director of Toyota Motors, had ordered the reduction to *three minutes*. By posing an "impossible" problem, Ohno ensured that a minimum number of preconceived ideas were brought to the problem, and hence the maximum degree of creativity was enabled.

Thus, to achieve effective change in a Manufacturing System, it is necessary for there to be pressure for change, within the system itself. However, whilst this is a *necessary* condition, it is by no means *sufficient*. Indeed, to take an analogy with pushing a door against a wedge, the very pressure for change may increase the capacity for resistance.

What is needed, therefore, are *Change Agents*, of whom Ohno is the supreme example. These are individuals with the mixture of creativity, enthusiasm and persistence to:

- question pre-conceived ideas; re-state the problems in a form amenable to effective solution;

- develop original solutions; and, last, but certainly not least

- sell the solutions to the decision makers.

As has been suggested, Manufacturing Systems are robust, adaptive organizations, accustomed to absorption of the forces of change. Enablers of change must probe the organization for its weaknesses, striking rapidly, precisely and unexpectedly, before the organization has time to respond and re-group, as a diamond cutter exploits fault planes. Like an exponent of *ju-jitsu*, the change agent must transform the strength and weight of the opponent into weaknesses.

Where are the change agents? How does an enterprise recruit them? Can the enterprise afford them? In answering these questions there is good news and bad news. Starting with the first question, they are already on the staff – which also deals with the second question. The manufacturing company which doesn't have change agents doesn't exist. Unfortunately, if the company didn't know the right answer, they have probably got problems – which brings us to the third question. By their very nature, companies cannot afford to have *unrecognized* change agents loose in the establishment. As has been described such people have the capability, if not the developed skills, to induce radical changes in the organization. In the absence of information to the contrary, it should be assumed that change agents are distributed throughout every organization, across boundaries of experience, intelligence and status. They are, however, not always active, perhaps only responding to the most extreme circumstances. For example, it is arguable that Simon Weston would still be just another guardsman if it were not for the horrific injuries sustained during the Falklands war which turned him into a campaigning hero for the disabled.

The effect of unrecognized change agents depends on the default underlying cultural attitude. In the organizations characterized by Theory X, there is an implicit assumption that only staff in the senior positions have the combination of skill, motivation and creativity to change the organization. Thus potentially useful contributors to the improvement of the company's efficiency are unrecognized, and either find other outlets for their creativity or remain indifferent to the future performance of the organization. Assuming that they restrict their activities within the organization, the former group are extremely likely to find opportunities for developing their talents in activities which undermine the integrity of the enterprise, particularly, for example, in official, or unofficial, trade union business.

The underlying principle of Theory Y is that all members of the organization are potential change agents. By implication, nothing should be done which would impede the exercise of the skills and creativity of the staff. The problem changes from having too few change agents to having too many. Further, it is over-optimistic to believe that every member of the workforce is fitted to the role. For example, Scase and Goffee [14] study the phenomenon of the *Reluctant Manager* in great detail. The general lesson which can be derived from this work is that many employees can provide a substantial and worthwhile contribution to the enterprise without acting as change agents.

In contrast to the two theories of McGregor, Theory Z is completely intolerant of change agents; the interests and creativity of the individual are subverted to the group. For example, the heroes of Japanese corporate culture have thrived in spite of, rather than because of, the prevailing national ethos. Their exploits are described by many authors, for example, Gilder [15]. Whereas such industrial giants as Honda, Sony and Matsushita are now seen as archetypal Japanese companies, their early progress was systematically impeded, in favour of the *zaibatsu* or *keiretsu* (described below), by Japan's powerful Ministry of International Trade and Industry, MITI, which dominates national industrial planning in Japan.

In the pursuit of its industrial strategy, MITI has been supported and encouraged by the large industrial and commercial groupings. Malcolm Trevor, of the Policy Studies Institute, perhaps the most authoritative British writer on Japanese industry, suggests that it is important to distinguish between the pre-war *zaibatsu*, the large integrated industrial – commercial conglomerates, and the post-war *keiretsu* which are confederations of companies with common interests rather than common ownership (Trevor [16] p25). Whilst acknowledging the authority of Trevor's opinion, it is certainly true that the autonomous companies comprising the modern *keiretsu* are often exactly the same companies which composed the earlier *zaibatsu*, which were dismantled by the occupying forces after the Second World War. Further, the nature of the cooperation is far from open. Even in the senior ranks of the Japanese Government, concern is being expressed at the apparent anti-competitive nature of these informal partnerships. James [17] takes a more pragmatic view of the *keiretsu* consistent with the viewpoint expressed here.

Internal Pressures

Internal change predominates in industries which undertake a substantial proportion of development of original equipment. Their competitive advantage derives from the pursuit of novelty and improvement in their products. Advances may originate in a variety of functional groups. In larger enterprises, formal responsibility for innovation is likely to be assigned to a research and development function. It is by no means unusual for this institutionalization of the responsibility for innovation to have a de-motivating effect on the other functions, perhaps leading to an adversarial relationship between research and development and the other functions. Although the source of radical change should never be regarded as the exclusive preserve of the research and development function, the other functional groups come into their own where incremental change is concerned. As Rosabeth Moss Kanter emphasized in her televised 1990 "Economist" lectures, the successful enterprise *depends* on the understanding that *everyone has a role to play in organizational change and every member of the workforce must believe this is so.* Incremental change depends on a continuing programme to improve designs, to enhance quality and to drive down costs.

Internal pressures for change are, perhaps, the most difficult to identify. Too often staff involved have been too close to the problems for too long, that they eventually lose the sense of appreciation of the benefits which may be derived from change. Living with inefficiency also leads to a climate of resignation to the deficiencies of the system. Further, there is often an inverse relationship between the system's initial responsiveness and the latent overall benefits which can be achieved once the change process is eventually set in motion.

At the other extreme, but equally common, there are many organizations where change, for the sake of change, has become a management obsession, having been pursued unsystematically and insensitively in the (almost universally mistaken) belief that eventually all will fall into place. Innovative management theories are applied superficially and without conviction, and given no chance to succeed before the next experiment is in progress, often with residual effects from the previous method prejudicing any hope of success. All too often, management rely on the expertise of external consultants to effect these changes disregarding, and implicitly belittling, the experience, skills and self-interest of the indigenous workforce. The response of the company's staff may vary from simply ignoring the activities of the consultants, to making temporary behavioural adjustments to humour the management – with the intention of reverting to the normal pattern of behaviour as soon as the intruders leave the premises, to systematic attempts to subvert the project. Whatever the response of the workforce, each new project is likely to have a smaller chance of success than its predecessor. This particular cycle of self-destructive behaviour was dubbed by the author 'consultancy poisoning'[19].

Managerial Pressures

In the current context, change stimuli will be classified into the usual vertical and a variety of less common types of horizontal influence. Mechanisms of change are often categorized as "top-down" or "bottom-up", consistent with the vertical perception of change stimuli based on classical theories of corporate hierarchy (see Woodward [20]). There are, however, some radical change events affecting the organization vertically, which are difficult to place into these categories. These include management buy-outs, where an operating subsidiary is purchased by its indigenous management, and management buy-ins, where an operating subsidiary is taken over by a new management team. These might be termed "middle outwards".

Top-down change is driven by Corporate Strategy. The general principles are widely known, and hence will not be reviewed in any detail here. The reader is referred to Latham and Sanders [21] or Sanders and Bradman [22]. In brief, Corporate Strategy is primarily the province of the senior executives of the enterprise, at board level or immediately below. The aim is the maximization of the value of the enterprise to its shareholders. This implies striking a balance between short-term income requirements and long-term viability. As described by Porter [23], Corporate Strategy entails two different activities: firstly, the business(es) which the enterprise should be in; and secondly, how the Corporate Centre should interact with its operating subsidiaries. The Corporate Centre can only justify its continued existence if it achieves synergies between its operating subsidiaries, i.e. the competitive performance of the group exceeds that which would accrue if the subsidiaries operated independently. As with all business decisions, the key question is: *"Where is the added value?"*. There is considerable merit in the viewpoint that the administrative centre of the organization should constantly take the role of an operating unit which has the primary purpose of selling services to the other subsidiaries, for which they have not got sufficient demand to make internal provision. This may take a number of forms, for example provision of information regarding market opportunities, centralized marketing facilities, loan provision, underwriting or brokerage, specialized technical support or legal services.

The consensus of a number of authoritative writers suggests that many boards of directors are not very good at Corporate Strategy. For example, Harvey-Jones [24] remarks:

'..unless you set it up that way, very few boards retain any control whatsoever over commercial decisions, and most boards of directors do not require to hear the details of very large contracts for purchases or sales.

'*... Equally notable is the fact that most boards of directors have no provision at all to review the general strategies and directions in which businesses are going and, apart from intervention in individual decision of investment, play only a small role in strategic direction.*' (ibid p 216)

Porter [23] provides quantitative evidence for the contention that many enterprises are singularly inept in their Corporate Strategy. He studied the track record of 33 large US enterprises over a period of some 36 years. He concludes:

'The track record of corporate strategies has been dismal. ... The corporate strategies of most companies have dissipated instead of created shareholder value.'

Porter proposes three tests for diversification to create shareholder value:

- **The attractiveness test**
  Diversification candidates must be structurally attractive or capable of being made so
- **The cost-of-entry test**
  Future profits must not be capitalized
- **The better-off test**
  Either the new activity or the enterprise itself must

gain competitive advantage from the association (preferably both).

In a work that is worthy of deeper study by the reader, Goold [25] has undertaken an extensive study of the strategic control processes of a substantial proportion of Britain's leading companies. He sees strategic control as an essential complement to financial control. Unfortunately, as his study demonstrates, many companies are continuing to organize their operations with absolutely minimal formal strategic planning. With the increasing recognition that "short-termism" is a serious problem in the strategic planning of many enterprises, the balance between budgetary control and strategic control is likely to improve. He quotes a Courtauld director:

'It's like playing the piano with both hands. You can get by if you're only playing with the financial control hand and forgetting the strategic control hand. You face a lot of risks if you are dealing only with the strategic control hand and not complementing it with the financial control hand. But for really top performance, you need to play with both hands.'

The commitment of Courtaulds to the strategic control process is evidenced by their corporate restructuring in October 1989. The vertically integrated group built by Lord Kearton in the 1960s and early 1970s was recognized as being inappropriately structured to ensure that it would thrive in market conditions which demanded adaptability and responsiveness. The solution entailed splitting the group into two independent companies, one primarily involved with manufacturing chemicals – for Courtaulds a relatively new venture – and the other textiles, the company's traditional business. The chairman, Sir Christopher Hogg, recognized that much of the senior management effort and energy, prior to the reconstruction, was wasted by trying to reconcile the strongly differing demands of the two businesses.

The two companies differ in a large number of respects including management structure, price/earnings ratio and market structure.

Textiles	*Chemicals*
National business	International business
Near (retail) market	Industrial customers
Driven by fashion	Driven by technology
Mature market	Strong growth market
Price-competitive	Compete on innovation
P/E ratio 9.5	P/E ratio 11
Investment funds internally generated	Requires substantial external funding
Turnover per employee £32000	Turnover per employee £80000
Profit per employee £1600	Profit per employee £6500

(Source: Rawsthorne and Marsh [25]).

The ascendancy of financial control measures over strategic control processes, described by Goold [26], is confirmed by another survey by KPMG Peat Marwick Management Consultants [27] who conclude:

'... emphasis on financial performance is likely to lead to a relatively narrow perception by senior managers of what is required in order for the organization to be successful.'

Both of these studies will be considered again, in greater detail, when the financing of change in manufacturing systems is considered.

The malaise of Corporate Strategy is not that the underlying techniques, such as SWOT (Strengths, Weaknesses, Opportunities, Threats), are unsound, but that they are applied uncritically and without empathy with the features of the business under consideration. This has been succinctly described as "form without meaning". All too often decisions are exclusively based on purely financial criteria, when applied to a single operating unit in isolation, without consideration of the consequential impact on the overall structure of the enterprise; i.e. there is a lack of "systems thinking". It is by no means unusual for the same simplistic financial measures, such as Return On Capital Employed (ROCE) or Return On Investment (ROI), to be applied indiscriminately whatever the underlying structure of the industry. Such an attitude can exclude consideration of even the most successful companies in specialist markets. For example, Teruyuki Yamazaki, son of the founder of MAZAK, currently the world's most successful machine tool builder, placed the success of his own company in perspective in the following terms:

'... in this business the investment of a large proportion of funds in production facilities and in research and development activities is essential. Therefore, the ratio of earnings to total capital is much lower than other manufacturing businesses *regardless of the prevailing economic conditions.*' [28]

Despite a compensating high ratio of gross profit to sales, the company believe that they would not be able to meet stock market expectations and have remained an unlisted company, even in Japan where investors traditionally take a long-term view.

Another recent example of a failure of an attractive Corporate Strategy is that of Coloroll. This enterprise certainly passed Porter's third test, and arguably the first. The strategy entailed horizontal integration of a number of businesses in the home furnishings market, including wallpaper, soft furnishings, crockery, cutlery and furniture. By offering consumers coordinated ranges of goods, the company was able to extend to the volume market the kind of choice which hitherto had only been available to the customers of expensive, and consequently exclusive, specialist suppliers. However the company failed Porter's second test quite comprehensively. The acquisition strategy was enabled by too high a gearing ratio, and, consequently, the loans proved to be unserviceable with increases in interest rates.

This caused both a rise in outgoings to service the loans themselves, and a fall in income, due to the squeeze on consumer spending. What is also of interest, in the current context, is the manner in which the corporate centre sought to impose a uniform operating style on the organization, characterized by the "*MBA barrow boys*". Their approach was typified by a simplistic and abrasively macho direction of the organization. Subsequent history has demonstrated that the individual businesses were viable but it is by no means certain that the product coordination can be preserved, as the businesses have been sold separately.

The second form of change is the bottom-up route. The potential contribution of subordinates is widely underestimated in Manufacturing Systems. This is particularly true where the workforce is supported by an innovative trade union organization. Trevor [16] attributes much of the credit for the success of the Toshiba plant to the cooperation of the trade union representative, Roy Sanderson of the Electrical, Electronic, Telecommunications and Plumbing Union. The agreements reached at Toshiba included no-strike deals, pendulum arbitration, and single status working. Trevor [16] quotes Sanderson:

'We have been attempting to remodel industrial relations in those industries where we have sole bargaining rights or major influence.'

He goes on to say:

'Our ambition was to create a pattern that was transferable to other manufacturing companies.'

Whilst it is true that Toshiba supported and encouraged the management at the Plymouth plant, it would be unreasonable to give them all of the credit. The primary drive of the Toshiba Manufacturing System was provided by Geoffrey Deith, the Managing Director, and David Smith, the Personnel Director. Deith's main inspiration was not a Japanese management model, but rather the innovative British management system developed at the Glacier Metal Company in the United Kingdom by Wilfred Brown (see, for example, Jacques and Brown [29]). The Glacier management policy was to steer a middle course between the extremes of the Taylorist and Human Relations (pioneered by Elton Mayo at the Hawthorne plant of Western Electric between 1927 and 1932 – see Roethlisberger and Dickson [30]) models of management behaviour.

Research presented by Daniel [31] provides strong support for the view that, in general, it is reasonable to assume that a company's workforce will be supportive of technical change, provided that full consultation is offered and management is seen to take their interests into account. It should be noted that this was the view of the management representatives in Daniel's study, as well as the researchers themselves and the workforce. Whilst the support of a progressive trade union is desirable it is, however, not essential.

By far the most difficult problem in initiating Organizational Change is the middle ground, characterized by the senior and middle management at business unit level. Too often, they are ill-equipped, in terms of training, skills and motivation, to fulfill the role of change agents. It is by no means unusual for the organization at the higher levels to change towards taking responsibility by business sectors rather than by functional background. Similarly, organization at shopfloor level is increasingly product oriented, with managers taking responsibility for a disparate multi-disciplinary group of workers rather than one with traditional craft-based demarcations and process-based production layouts. In between are the company's middle management, often still organized by functional responsibilities, who operate in an organizational no-mans-land, with their previous lines of communication cut both above and below. All too often, managers are working in jobs for which they have no formal training, both prior to entering employment with the enterprise and, perhaps more importantly, subsequently. Indeed, a significant proportion of British industrial managers have had no relevant training whatsoever (see, for example, Clutterbuck and Crainer [32] pp66-68). The issue of training will be discussed at some length later in the text, in particular the studies by Handy [33] and Constable and McCormick [34]). Harvey-Jones [24] suggests that this is particularly true for company directors, citing the lack of guidance which he received on his promotion to the board of directors of Imperial Chemical Industries, a company which is widely regarded as exemplary in its approach to training and career development.

Thus the middle managers of the enterprise may provide a major stumbling block in the path to change. Not only may they be poorly motivated to implement change instructions passed from the Corporate Centre (Scase and Goffee [14]), they often cannot be guaranteed even to comprehend them sufficiently. However, at the other extreme, many companies are reluctant to employ people straight from school or college because this also requires a commitment to training that they are unwilling to provide. Indeed, they are encountering the problems in their middle management precisely because of their reluctance to undertake rational training activities. Perhaps the most common approach to this problem, therefore, has been to make these non-performing managers redundant, replacing them with younger, formally trained, staff recruited from outside the organization.

This is, however, proving to be an unsustainable strategy. Firstly, such recruits are of questionable loyalty, since they have been recruited from another company which, presumably, has invested some time and effort in their training. Secondly, the indigenous staff are likely to be demotivated by external recruitment, either because of the perception that their own skills are implicitly undervalued or because of the reduction of their own promotion opportunities. Thirdly, particularly for engineers, there is a shrinking pool of available talent. This is true internationally but is particularly so in Britain, where a significantly smaller proportion of young people of the right calibre, or any quality for that matter, are entering the engineering profession. Last, but not least, although the managers under threat may not be performing they often possess an irreplaceable knowledge of the workings of the organization, its products, its procedures, its customer relations, etc., and particularly memories of previous managerial failures and the understanding of, and the capability to manipulate, the informal processes of the enterprise.

Technological Pressures

Internal technological pressures may originate from a variety of sources, for example design, production engineering, quality or production management. The particular stimuli appropriate for change initiation are dependent on the nature of the company's products, including their complexity, volume, value and variety, the methods of organization of production, and the processes used, both current and alternative.

Radical change is typified by the posing of fundamental questions concerning the objectives of the manufacturing systems. A supreme example of this is the case of the production of constant velocity joints, for front wheel drive vehicles, at the Hardy-Spicer company in the United Kingdom. The initial production process for these components involved extensive machining from (relatively) crudely dimensioned bought-in forgings. The question which manufacturing management asked themselves was: *"What are we making?"* A little lateral thinking led to an unexpected, but accurate answer. Of the material entering the plant, over 50% left as *swarf or scrap* components. They had realized that they were infringing one of the basic rules of production engineering – that you should put material where it is needed rather than remove it where it isn't. The company was able to change to a near-net process for production of the unfinished components, i.e. the dimensions of the blanks were close enough to those of the finished components that only a single finishing grinding operation was required.

Whilst this was a relatively simple technological solution to a straightforward technological question, the impact on the manufacturing systems of the enterprise transcended the technical domain, reinforcing the view expressed earlier that Daniel and Millward's [1] separation of categories of technical change (Advanced Technical Change, Conventional Technical Change and Organizational Change) is perhaps too artificial to be of any substantial validity in the current context. Viewed according to the strict interpretation of Daniel and Millward's categories, Hardy-Spicer's problem was one of conventional technical change. The impact of the imaginative, yet relatively straightforward, technological problem consequentially presented a challenging, and potentially devastating, array of problems for the organizational structure of the enterprise. From a position of a multi-stage, multi-operation, multi-process, metal cutting manufacturing system, the production route was reduced to what had formerly been the finishing operations. This (potentially) had the effects of:

- Reducing the scale of the production area required.

- Reducing the scale of the production scheduling problem such that it was *comparatively* insignificant.

- Rendering redundant a substantial proportion of the manufacturing plant.

- Rendering redundant a substantial proportion of the shopfloor workforce.

- Changing the required skill profile at a number of levels of the organization.

- Significantly reducing the role, and hence potentially the authority and status, of the staff in the management of the production-based functions.

- Significantly increasing the role, and hence potentially the authority and status, of the staff in the management of the procurement and quality-based functions.

- Reducing the inventory by reducing the number of operations, and hence machining time and, usually more significant in batch manufacturing, inter-operation waiting times.

As has been described previously, to guarantee change requires the confluence of authority, resources, expertise and motivation. In this case the staff with the necessary expertise to identify the opportunity for radical change were precisely the same group who had most to lose in authority, status and perhaps ultimately their livelihood. The Hardy-Spicer example is quite well-known, perhaps principally because it is the exception rather than the rule. What cannot even be estimated is how many technological managers have wavered, and subsequently drawn back from such a threat to their position.

References

[1] Daniel, W. W. and Millward, N., *Workplace Industrial Relations in Britain*, Heinemann, London 1984.

[2] Imai, M., *Kaizen: The Key to Japan's Competitive Success*, Random House, New York 1986.

[3] Foster, R. N., *Innovation: the Attacker's Adavantage*, Macmillan, London 1986.

[4] Gallagher, C. C., "The history of batch production and functional factory layout", *Chartered Mechanical Engineer*, April, pp73-76, 1981.

[5] Johnson, H. T. and Kaplan, R. S., *Relevance Lost: The Rise and Fall of Management Accounting*, Harvard Business School Press, Boston, MA 1987.

[6] Naisbitt, J., *Megatrends*, Macdonald, London 1984.

[7] Jaffe, W. J., "Standardization and Scientific Management", *Mechanical Engineering*, April 1984, pp56-59.

[8] McGregor, D., *The Human Side of Enterprise*, McGraw-Hill, New York 1960.

[9] Ouichi, W., *Theory Z: How American Business can meet the Japanese Challenge*, Addison Wesley, New York 1981.

[10] Tribus, M., "Deming's Way", *Mechanical Engineering*, January 1988, pp26-31.

[11] Ishikawa, K., Translated D J Lu, *What is Total Quality Control? – the Japanese Way*, Prentice-Hall, New Jersey 1985.

[12] Burbidge, J. L., "Whatever Happened to Group Technology", *Management Today*, September 1978, pp87-89&193.

[13] Shingo, S., *Study of the Toyota Production System from Industrial Engineering Viewpoint*, Japan Management Association, Tokyo 1981.

[14] Scase, R. and Goffee, R., *Reluctant Managers: Their Work and Lifestyles*, Unwin-Hyman, London 1989

[15] Gilder, G., *The $pirit of Enterprise*, Simon and Schuster, New York 1984.

[16] Trevor, M., *Toshiba's New British Company: Competitiveness through Innovation in Industry*, Policy Studies Institute, London 1988.

[17] James, B. G., *Trojan Horse: The Ultimate Japanese Challenge to Western Industry*, W H Allen-Mercury, London 1989.

[18] Prahalad, C.K. and Hamel, G., "The Core Competence of the Corporation", *Harvard Business Review*, May-June 1990, pp79-91.

[19] Brandon, J. A., "Where consultants fall down", *Management Today*, May 1988, pp109-119.

[20] Woodward, J., *Industrial Organization: Theory and Practice*, Oxford University Press, 1965.

[21] Latham, F. W. and Sanders, G. S., *Urwick Orr: On Management*, Heinemann, London 1980.

[22] Sanders, G. S. and Bradman, R. H., "Corporate Strategies for the Future", in D Lock and N Farrow (Editors), *The Gower Handbook of Management*, Gower, Aldershot, England 1988.

[23] Porter, M. E., "From Competitive Advantage to Corporate Strategy", *McKinsey Quarterly*, Spring 1988, pp35-66.

[24] Harvey-Jones, J., *Making it Happen: Reflections on Leadership*, Collins, London 1988.

[25] Rawsthorn, A. and Marsh, P., "Two hope to thrive better than one", *Financial Times*, October 31 1989.

[26] Goold, M. (with Quinn, J. J.), *Strategic Control: Milestones for Long-term Performance*, The Economist Books/Hutchinson, London 1990.

[27] *Information for Strategic Management: A Survey of Leading Companies*, KPMG Peat Marwick Management Consultants, 1990.

[28] Kuba, Y., *Master of Manufacturing Technology: the 70-Year History of MAZAK*, N D Publications, Tokyo 1989.

[29] Jacques, E. and Brown, W., *Glacier Project Papers*, Heinemann London, 1971.

[30] Roethlisberger, F. and Dickson, W., *Management and the Worker*, Harvard University Press, Cambridge MA 1939.

[31] Daniel, W. W., *Workplace Industrial Relations and Technical Change*, Frances Pinter/ Policy Studies Institute, London 1987.

[32] Clutterbuck, D. and Crainer, S., *The Decline and Rise of British Industry*, W H Allen-Mercury, London 1988.

[33] Handy, C., *The Making of Managers: a Report on Management Education, Training and Development in the USA, West Germany, France, Japan and the UK*, National Economic Development Office, London 1987.

[34] Constable, J. and McCormick, R., *The Making of British Managers*: Report to the British Institute of Management and the Confederation of British Industry into Management Training, Education and Development, British Institute of Management, 1987.

4

Structure of the Manufacturing Enterprise

Management Structure

Management structures are rarely designed from scratch and, perhaps, even more rarely are they designed without significant prejudices and preconceptions which are often based on the principle that anything which differs from the present structure is bound to be superior. Such a jaundiced viewpoint usually contains rather more than a grain of truth. Management structures which have been undisturbed for a period of time are susceptible to a number of ailments including, but not restricted to, complacency and vested interest.

Take, for example, the case of Ferranti International [1]. After a traumatic period in the company's history, involving the disastrous takeover of an American subsidiary, the company turned to an appointee from outside the company, Eugene Anderson, as its new chairman in February 1990. His appointment was largely due to his previous success in restoring the fortunes of the Johnson Matthey group after similarly injudicious trading decisions in 1984. (These are described in Heller [2] pp218-9).

Anderson's approach is exemplary. After being appointed on a Friday, he presented the directors with a list of personal objectives on the following Monday. These included the setting of management incentives, quality improvement and financial targets. As with any external appointment the crucial prerequisite is the attainment of the support of the company's existing staff. This is particularly important whenever the use of external management consultants is contemplated, as in this case.

Anderson described the key problem in the following terms:

> '.. people forget what they are in business for. They forget that the organization has to be disciplined and focussed, with everyone working together to fulfil their goals. If that begins to fall down, there's trouble lurking around the corner.'

Involvement of the indigenous staff was achieved by setting up task forces, each to examine a different facet of the business, comprising both consultants and managers. Different task forces examined corporate strategy, operations management and the operating divisions. The final plan was approved after a meeting of the senior management of the company where the (approximately sixty) managers were given opportunities to discuss the proposals and recommend modifications. The managers were split into five discussion groups and care was taken to separate existing partnerships – although the groups chose their own chairmen – to reduce the chances of the perpetuation of historical interests. These were described by Anderson in the following terms:

> 'There was not much logic as to why certain businesses were based in certain divisions. ... The divisions themselves were run like baronies. There was not much interference from the centre.'

The changes had three main facets:

A new reward system, based on four levels of performance: group, division, business unit and individual. The system is designed to relate to factors over which the individual has direct influence, i.e. within a business unit the emphasis would be on the performance of the unit and on the achievement of personal objectives.

Better definition and strengthening of the corporate centre, whilst devolving more power to the operating units. In particular, central review of contracts was instigated to counter a particular historical weakness of the group.

Restructuring of the business into three divisions, with rationally grouped product areas, rather than the five previous divisions with product allocations which were based more on history and expediency than on rational planning.

Only time will tell if the restructuring exercise in Ferranti has been successful. In Ferranti's case, as with so many other business rationalizations, restructuring was forced on the organization by the prospect of imminent failure. If the business does fail, however, it will not be because of Anderson's initial approach, which is exemplary. In particular the company's management were involved at all stages of the process, from the diagnosis of the organization's problems to the development of the strategies for their solution. Particularly important was the systematic approach to building consensus. In this respect distinguishing between decisions reached collectively, as in this case, rather than collective decision making is important (see Heller [1]). The Japanese excel in the former, epitomised by the *ringi* philosophy. As described by Heller (op cit pp40-46), this system seems tortuous, with proposals passed down through all of the layers of the organization for comment before being passed back up for approval, with the proposals for the problem's solution being approved at each level before the final decision is reached. (See also Skapinker [2]).

Devolution to Strategic Business Units (SBUs)

The general trend in the structure of manufacturing organizations is towards reorganization of the enterprise as autonomous business units. This is due, in the overwhelming majority of cases, as much to fashion as to original strategic planning. All too often, such strategies are inadequately planned and, consequently, are susceptible to a number of serious structural defects. It is not surprising, therefore, that companies very often follow a period of devolution with one of recentralization. However, it should be recognized that the ebb and flow of control within business organizations is a natural feature of their healthy existence. What is important is that the changes in the structure of the organization should be carefully planned and rigorously controlled. Prahalad and Hamel [3] have argued strongly that the trend to business units puts the survival of the organization as a whole at risk:

'When the organization is conceived of as a multiplicity of SBUs, no single business may feel responsible for maintaining a viable position in core products nor be able to justify the investment required to build world leadership in some core competence. In the absence of a more comprehensive view imposed by corporate management, SBU managers will tend to underinvest.'

There are certain essential prerequisites for successful devolution of the management of a business to autonomous business units.

- Firstly, there is a basic requirement, often described as "critical mass", i.e. the turnover of the business unit must be adequate to support the essential functions of the unit. These essential functions will vary, dependent on the product, its process technology and its proximity to the market.

- Secondly, for such a strategy to be successful the cooperation and consent of the management and other employees of the business unit is essential. After all, it will be their responsibility to make the new business unit successful.

- Thirdly, the process of transition demands careful and considered management.

Turning to the third condition first it is a common mistake when business organizations initiate a plan to transfer control to autonomous business units, for the change to be required of all of the business units simultaneously. This may have a number of undesirable effects including, but not restricted to, an overload on the management resources of the corporate centre. This may lead both to a loss of control of the devolution process and needless repetition of the same mistakes. Consequently, an opportunity is lost for the organization to learn from the process of devolution to one business unit and apply that knowledge to the subsequent units. There is, however, one attractive feature of the simultaneous devolution strategy, that it will minimize the capability of the corporate centre to intervene to perpetuate unnecessary controls of the business units.

Critical mass implies the capacity of the organization to survive, and hopefully to thrive, without substantial support and control from the corporate centre. System responsiveness, widely regarded as critically important in the success of manufacturing systems, depends on reduction of the need for external approval before undertaking management activities. As was seen in the Ferranti case, described above, it may be necessary for some controls to continue to be exercised from the corporate centre, but this should generally be seen as an exception and the reasons for such a course of action should be clearly articulated. Ideally, the retention of functions by the corporate centre should be proposed by the business unit rather than group management.

Planning Devolution

The planning of devolution conforms to the first law of management: it is simple – but it isn't easy. It is all too easy to throw the baby of systems coherence out with the bathwater of centralized control. Such problems respond to well-known techniques such as SWOT grids, i.e. the analysis both of current position and proposed actions in terms of *Strengths*, *Weaknesses*, *Opportunities* and *Threats*. Take, for example, the case of a company which manufactures power train components. The whole range of the company's products is likely to include motors, gearboxes, clutches, etc., each of which requires different manufacturing methods, materials, skills and management strategies. It is likely that the company, particularly if it has been previously strongly managed from the centre, will be seen by its customers as a provider of systems rather than components. There is likely to be a perception, however inaccurate, that the products from the one company are more likely to be compatible than equivalent components bought from a number of different suppliers. In terms of this *Strength* of the existing corporate structure, the devolved organization would have a corresponding *Weakness* unless specific measures were taken to counter this problem. For example, a unit could be established with the express objective of exploiting the historic corporate image. (Although this would be a poor option in many cases.)

Restructuring of the organization is, in itself, a significant threat to its survival. Faced with a choice between a gradual decline, which is likely to be essentially imperceptible, and a high-profile, but high-risk, restructuring option, it is perhaps understandable why so many boards choose the "soft option".

Kanter describes the adverse effects which can be anticipated during a period of corporate restructuring:

'Costs of confusion
Misinformation
Emotional leakage
Loss of energy
Loss of key resources
Breakdown of initiative
Weakened faith in leaders' ability to deliver, and the need for scapegoats.'

(Kanter [3] pp62-64).

As has been suggested, the process of devolution may place an intolerable load on the enterprise, leading to either total failure or, more commonly, retrenchment and recentralization. Often the staff most identified with the devolution strategy are sacrificed – particularly the heads of the business units, who are likely to be reluctant scapegoats – when the fault may be primarily the reluctance, and perhaps downright obstruction, of the headquarters staff to relinquish control. In the case of total failure the old surgical adage often applies: 'The operation was a success, unfortunately the patient died!'

It is worthwhile to consider the circumstances under which an organization would wish to centralize its operations. As Kanter [4] describes, in the case of Apple Computers, centralization may be the only sensible answer where there is a breakdown in the internal discipline of an enterprise.

If the achievement of critical mass is a criterion in enabling devolution, then, conversely, failure to maintain critical mass is grounds for reconsidering the autonomy of a business unit. The conclusion may well be other than centralizing control, indeed it would usually be a poor option, diverting staff whose primary role should be strategic planning into the operational domain.

The solution at Ferranti was the placing of the activities that were regarded as valuable, but small, into the division with the most diverse range of activities.

Returning to the basic systems model of manufacturing, the quality of the management structure of a business unit (or any other management entity, for that matter) can be assessed, at least in part, by quantifying the number and complexity of its input-output relationships.

- What are the links between the business unit and the corporate centre? What proportion of the business unit's input-output relationships are accounted for by communication with the corporate centre? Is this proportion consistent with healthy operating performance?

- Why are they linked in this way? Could links be eliminated, amalgamated or simplified?

- Is the decision-making process of the business unit dependent on consent from the corporate centre? If so, is it necessary? Does the link to the centre cause threats to the responsiveness of the business unit? If so, how could the decision-making power be devolved?

The Hanson Trust is often regarded largely as a corporate raider. This perception is based on their enviable track record in contested takeovers, and subsequent breakup, of the corporate dinosaurs which the conglomerates of the sixties and seventies became. Often the proceeds of the sales of just one or two subsidiaries were sufficient to finance the takeover, with all subsequent transactions yielding pure profit. What is unusual for a pure corporate raider is the number, and diversity, of businesses which Hanson has kept under management. Indeed, Michael Porter, in a much quoted and influential paper (Porter [5]), questioned whether there was a significant danger of Hanson becoming as unwieldy as the conglomerates on which it had preyed. In the time since Porter's paper there has been little evidence of the corporate atrophy which Porter feared. Indeed, the virtual demise of the corporate get-rich-quick schemes of the 1980s, funded by deceit and driven by greed, (including the contested leveraged buy-out and management buy-out) has led to new opportunities for Hanson.

What is of interest here, however, is how Hanson has continued to manage such a diverse portfolio of subsidiaries with such sustained success. For example, SLD Pumps was acquired by Hanson in 1967 and has seen its profits rise by 18% compound throughout the 1980s and return on capital employed risen to 55%, despite an annual capital investment budget of £1m. Such performance is hardly consistent with Hanson's image as an asset stripper.

The introduction of a new company into the Hanson way of doing things proceeds in two stages: tactical and strategic. Firstly, SWOT analysis is undertaken with particular attention given to restoring the morale of the organization and the identification of potentially effective management. The chief operating officer, UK, Tony Alexander, is quoted in the following terms:

> 'Three months after we arrive, there must be significant changes – after that newness is a wasting asset. You get the easiest changes in that time.'

This is consistent with the Pareto principle, that (typically) the first twenty per cent of effort in a management task will result in eighty per cent of the realizable benefit.

On conclusion of the tactical phase Alexander will have little, if anything, further to do with the enterprise. Control is passed to the divisional chief executive whose role is to simplify the corporate structure, decentralize to accountable business units and set achievable objectives. There is substantial pressure to simplify the management structure, particularly in terms of the reduction of management layers. Otherwise the executives of the business units are largely autonomous, being measured against 'demanding but realistic' budgets which are proposed by the business units themselves. Business units are measured against the trading performance of the relevant sector. Incentives are layered, with those of junior employees being triggered at a lower level of performance than those for more senior managers. There is a general, and simple, criterion for capital investment of a payback of four years although there is some flexibility in this rule for a well argued case.

Part of Porter's commentary can be interpreted as questioning whether the operation of corporate headquarters adds value to the operating performance of the constituent businesses. David Ireland, of brokers Hoare Govett, estimates that Hanson is trading at a premium of 6% on operating assets, which is, presumably, a suitable indicator of the contribution of the corporate centre. (See Porter [4] and Holberton [6].)

For comparison, at the opposite extreme, the case of Thorn Lighting is a supreme example of how not to manage corporate strategy. In May 1990 *Management Today* [7] announced Thorn Lighting as Best Overall Company in the Business in Europe competition.

> 'The overall winner, Thorn Lighting, won the unanimous vote of the judges for a strategy that was almost daunting in its thoroughness, yet retained the flexibility of commercial opportunism.'

Managing Director, Hamish Brice was quoted: 'We regard Europe as our home market.'

Hardly was the ink dry when the Thorn group announced the sale of its lighting division to GTE of the US. Despite having met their targets for market penetration, their primary criterion for competitiveness, the group suggested that the lighting interests were not internationally competitive, being too dependent on the UK market.

By September, Michael Skapinker of the *Financial Times*, was able to report that the deal with GTE had not been consummated. The group now planned to '... make a success of the business by entering joint ventures and rationalizing its manufacturing side.' Not surprisingly, Thorn shares dropped 5% in one day.

It is by no means certain that all of the blame rests with Thorn. Indeed, the study by Prahalad and Hamel [3], cited earlier, contrasts the strategic planning at Japanese NEC and US GTE, noting particularly that 'No such clarity of strategic intent and strategic architecture appeared to exist at GTE.' The problems with Thorn have occurred despite the new management team at GTE which Prahalad and Hamel suggested may have improved GTE's corporate strategy.

Whoever was the main culprit, the staff at Thorn Lighting have effectively experienced two episodes of corporate restructuring, albeit abortive. The corporate centre has, firstly, indicated a lack of confidence in their long-term viability. Subsequently, the group has not only questioned the competitiveness of the division in its existing form, but also restricted its strategic horizons by the defensive rationalization of its manufacturing operations. The workforce must feel the Sword of Damocles hanging over them, in terms of other plans for the sale of the business or, quite possibly, closure of the division.

The lack of confidence of the corporate centre in the viability of the business must be seriously prejudicial to the morale, and consequently the operating effectiveness of the lighting division. Failure to dispel the reservations about the long-term future of the division effectively turns the uncertainty into a self-fulfilling prophesy.

Internal Relationships Within Business Units

Having examined its input-output relationships, the second facet of the organization of a system is its internal structure. Rather than consider the structure of the business unit in terms of the levels of seniority, corresponding to the usual perception of the organization as a classical hierarchy, it is of value initially to consider the activities of the business unit in the context of planning horizon, i.e. strategic, tactical and operational. This will enable the consideration of the principle, often advocated but less frequently implemented, of devolution of authority to the staff most involved with the effects of the decision. Conventional thinking would attribute close correspondence between the layers of the classical hierarchy and the planning horizon, with executive management having responsibility for strategic planning, middle management providing tactical support and supervisory staff undertaking the operational role.

For many manufacturing organizations the dissemination of authority throughout the enterprise requires a radical change in corporate culture. The Toyota Production System, where according to Shingo [8] '... after three days temporary workers are able to work *independently*', demonstrates that total devolution is achievable, with every production worker having the authority to stop production when a quality problem is identified.

There are, however, few areas of management about which more 'twaddle' has been written than corporate culture. In particular, sweeping generalizations are made on the basis of what is only a superficial analysis of a successful enterprise. Stereotypes abound, not least the idea of a seamless and unique "Japanese" system of management. Consider, for example, the three giants of the Japanese motor industry. Whereas Honda's strength is its flair and creativity in design, Toyota relies on its excellence in manufacturing technology and production management and Nissan's strength is its market awareness. Whilst

Nissan has largely followed and benefited from the strong national industrial programmes, both Toyota and Honda have thrived in spite of, rather than because of, intervention by government agencies to impede the execution of their corporate strategies. (For the early history of Toyota see Parkinson [9]).

An experienced viewpoint on corporate culture, which reflects that of the author, is that of Harvey-Jones:

> 'I find myself intolerant of management books that seek to prescribe exactly 'how it should be done'. My own experience shows that there are many different ways of leading an industrial company. I have worked with leaders whose style is so totally different to my own that I have found it incomprehensible that they achieve results, but nevertheless they do. ...' (Harvey-Jones [10] p16).

Whereas the prevailing philosophy in the management literature is management by consensus, it should be realized that many of the most successful manufacturing organizations have been run by despots for a major proportion of their existence. Whilst consensus management matches the author's personal style and inclinations, perhaps reflected too strongly in the current work, it may well be true that the transition from authoritarian to consensus management is more of a risk than perpetuation of the status quo.

Deal and Kennedy [11] describe the 'Organization of the Future' in the following terms:

- 'small task-focussed work units (ten to twenty persons maximum)

- each with economic and management control over its own destiny

- interconnected with larger entities through benign computer and communication links

- and bonded into larger companies through strong cultural bonds'.

Although this model will be subject to criticism here, it would be completely wrong to infer that Deal and Kennedy's work came into the category of the "twaddle" described above.

In many respects, Deal and Kennedy's *atomised organization*, described above, corresponds to the assumptions in the model with which any manufacturing organization would be analyzed. Indeed, it matches the approach of the computer programming methodology of *Object Oriented Programming Systems* which is the subject of considerable excitement in the modelling of complex systems. In practice, however, this idealized model has serious deficiencies.

Firstly, as anyone familiar with the use of computers, and particularly their communication links, will be aware there is no such thing as a benign computer or, *a fortiori*, communication between computers. Many of the problems which bedevil computers are primarily the result of poor discipline, for example the chicken-and-egg of the general inadequacy of standards and the wilful failure of the manufacturers and software suppliers to apply them.

Other problems are, however, inherent in the nature of communication systems. For example, the relationship between the amount of traffic in a telecommunications system and the number of subscribers is non-linear, i.e. if the number of subscribers is doubled then the volume of traffic is not necessarily doubled accordingly. One subscriber leads to no network traffic; two need no switching and three may lead to engaged/busy conditions. Further, demand is a stochastic function, i.e. the instant that a subscriber makes a connection is not predictable (unless you happen to be getting out of the shower). The combination of stochastic events and non-linear systems is the main prerequisite for the occurrence of chaotic dynamics, which may be anything but benign. Chaotic effects are, by their very nature, unpredictable in their onset. Often there are threshold requirements, below which systems behave predictably and beyond which the chaotic dynamics occur. Whilst much of the mathematics of chaotic dynamics is highly abstract, and currently inapplicable, there are instances of the occurrence of chaotic effects in existing telephone networks. When a group of networks in the USA was integrated a series of serious fault conditions occurred. These were of a chaotic nature, which could not have been predicted from either the design models of the individual networks or their behaviour under normal operating conditions.

The basic rationale of devolution is simple: give staff the belief that their contribution is valued by the organization and they will justify that confidence by providing a valuable contribution. This is the essential driving force of the Japanese *ringi* system. Ford (UK) have recently proved that it isn't necessary to be Japanese to excite enthusiasm in the workforce for self-improvement. Employees were offered a range of study courses, both vocational and general interest, at company premises but in their own time. The level of the courses ranged from basic numeracy and literacy to degree equivalent. Many of the students had educational track records generally perceived as failure. Participation levels exceeded Ford's wildest dreams – a proportion approximately five times their estimate of five per cent.

In many respects Deal and Kennedy's viewpoint is consistent with the general trend in industrial organization. Atomized organizations may, however, suffer from a number of structural defects. These have been addressed by Prahalad and Hamel [3], in the *Harvard Business Review*.

'The fragmentation of core competencies becomes inevitable when a diversified company's information systems, patterns of communication, career paths, and processes of strategy development do not transcend SBU lines. We believe that senior management should spend a significant amount of its time developing a corporate-wide strategic architecture that establishes objectives for competence building.'

For a comprehensive overview of good practice in strategic control processes the reader is referred to the recent work by Goold [12].

References

[1]   Skapinker, M., "The man with the task of regenerating Ferranti", *Financial Times*, August 29, 1990

[2]   Heller, R., *The Decision Makers*, Coronet/Hodder and Stoughton, London 1989.

[3]   Prahalad, C. K. and Hamel, G., "The Core Competence of the Corporation", *Harvard Business Review*, May-June, 1990, pp79-91.

[4]   Kanter, R. M., *When Giants Learn to Dance: Mastering the Challenge of Strategy, Management and Careers in the 1990s*, Simon and Schuster, New York 1989.

[5]   Porter, M., "From Competitive Advantage to Corporate Strategy", *Harvard Business Review*, 65(3), May-June 1987, pp43-59.

[6]   Holberton, S., "Under the skin of a takeover artiste extraordinaire", *Financial Times*, August 22, 1990.

[7]   Business in Europe Awards 1990, *Management Today*, May 1990, pp44-75.

[8]   Shingo, S., *Study of the Toyota Production System from Industrial Engineering Viewpoint*, Japan Management Association, Tokyo 1981.

[9]   Parkinson, C. N., *Big Business*, Weidenfeld and Nicolson, London 1974.

[10] Harvey-Jones, J., *Making it Happen: Reflections on Leadership*, Collins, London 1988.

[11] Deal, T. and Kennedy, A., *Corporate Cultures: The Rites and Rituals of Corporate Life*, Addison-Wesley, New York 1982.

[12] Goold, M. (with Quinn, J. J.), "Strategic Control: Milestones for Long-term Performance", *The Economist* Books/Hutchinson, London 1990.

5

Changes in the Organization of Manufacture

As has been described, the majority of the enterprises which contemplate radical change in their manufacturing systems are more likely be in the position of considering change from functional to product-oriented organizations. This is, however, not always the case and it is important to recognize the circumstances under which companies should evaluate the benefits (and conversely the costs) of the more unconventional approach.

There is a well-known history of a placebo effect in organizational change, although it is more commonly called the Hawthorne effect, from the studies by Elton Mayo at the Hawthorne plant of Western Electric in the late 1920s and early 1930s. (See Roethlisberger and Dickson [1]). As might be expected, in a series of controlled studies Mayo found that performance improved when the working environment improved. What was less easily explained was that performance also improved when the working environment was changed for the worse.

Kanter [2] discusses at some length the case of the radical changes found necessary in the corporate structure at Apple Computer. As with many enterprises in the world of information technology, Apple had been founded by a small group of creative, highly talented and motivated entrepreneurs. As with many other pioneers of computer technology, for example Bill Gates of Microsoft, a precocious teenager's hobby became a multi-million dollar business. Unfortunately, the talents of creating businesses are by no means the same skills that are required to ensure their long-term viability. Kanter [2] describes how Apple had, by 1983, become a number of businesses-within-businesses, with product-centred groups competing aggressively for the same scarce resources, without any concern for the security of the overall enterprise. Internal competition is not, however, in itself a bad thing, provided that there is overall coordination, that the groups recognize that there is a substantial difference between healthy rivalry and the kind of viscious infighting that can occur if cooperation breaks down and, last but not least, that the needs of the customer are not ignored. What made the position of the company particularly hazardous was that Steve Jobs, one of the original co-founders of the company was one of the principal protagonists.

There are two basic issues in the change of manufacturing organization: firstly, the identification of a suitable new organizational structure; secondly, the definition and implementation of the chosen strategy. Although simplistic, the basic approach of SWOT (Strengths-Weaknesses-Opportunities-Threats) analysis has much to recommend it. It cannot be emphasized strongly enough, however, that it is absolutely essential to apply the technique to the *existing* organization in addition to any candidate alternative structures.

Whilst the actual SWOT evaluation of changes in management structure in an enterprise is likely to be substantially more specific and detailed than described here, the following generic issues are likely to be considered.

Existing Organisation

- *Strengths*

    Developed in response to the manufacturing experience of the enterprise.

Informal structures may complement, and compensate for, serious structural faults in the formal structure of the organization.

* *Weaknesses*

May not be responsive to market conditions.

May impede the introduction of new technology or management practices.

* *Opportunities*

Incremental change in production technology or production management will not be disrupted by uncertainties as to authority or accountaibity.

* *Threats*

Tends to reinforce existing perceptions of the invulnerability of the enterprise.

New Organization

* *Strengths*

Hawthorne effect: changes may have beneficial effects purely because they add interest to the working environment.

* *Weaknesses*

Introduction of any non-trivial change in the structure of a manufacturing organization is likely to lead to (often serious) unforeseen problems.

* *Opportunities*

Existing restrictive practices may be called into

question when the workforce recognizes the priority for consensus in progressing to a new organizational structure.

• *Threats*

The importance of informal structures, in compensating for the defects and inefficiencies of the existing organization, may be misjudged.

Management commitment to the changes in the structure of the organization may divert attention from other urgent problems which threaten the enterprise.

Organizational Structure

It is implicit, in the discussion presented previously, that there is a broad consensus in favour of development of modular management structures. Even General Electric, with its long (and arguably successful) history of centralized strategic planning under Jack Welch, has recognized the value of reducing the capability of the corporate centre to intervene (interfere?) in the affairs of its subsidiaries. (See Goold [3]).

The essential features of successful modular management structures include:

Critical mass, ie the management unit must be sufficiently large to be able to undertake its normal operating role without reliance on external support.

Management must be able to achieve their objectives within the planning horizon of the operating unit.

Sufficient resources must be available to enable the operating unit to develop its own strategies for management of its manufacturing systems.

Management must be empowered to develop all aspects of their business planning, including its strategic and operational aspects.

Procedures must be introduced to prevent unnecessary intervention from the corporate centre.

Reporting requirements must be reduced and simplified, to ensure that the minimum of effort is necessary to satisfy financial and strategic control processes.

The consequence of the above requirements is that there are both upper and lower limits on the size of an effective operating unit. These cannot be prescribed generally, however, since they are dependent both on the structure of the market, the chosen management culture and also the technological constraints of materials and processes.

As described by Prahalad and Hamel [4], management within business units are (perhaps unconsciously) likely to subvert the long-term viability of the enterprise, in favour of those aspects which are consistent with their own estimation of the corporate centre's perception of their performance. This is commonly viewed in terms of standardized short-term performance measures. Marsh [5] suggests that the priorites of British and American managers, who typically remain in the same job for three years and with the same company for an average of five years, may be a major discriminator between the performance of Western and Japanese management. This issue will be discussed in much greater detail when the effects of investment appraisal methodologies are considered.

Change Strategy

Abrupt change throughout a manufacturing organization is almost always a high risk strategy. It requires an intense management effort, which may be stretched beyond its capacity to recover if managerial resources are too thinly distributed. Unfortunately it is by no means unusual for this to be the desperate action of a company which is already in serious difficulties. In which case it is more often than not fatal. Even when this approach is used in companies where failure is not imminent, an opportunity is sacrificed to use the knowledge gained from one area to improve the introduction of the changed organizational structure elsewhere in the enterprise.

In organizations where there is a strong existing corporate culture there is considerable merit in introducing experimental variations in the organization of the enterprise in subsidiaries remote from the mainstream operational centre of the company. This has the dual effect of isolating the experimental facility from overwhelming pressures to conform to the mainstream corporate culture and protecting the core business from unforseen, and potentially disastrous, effects of radical experimentation with organizational structures.

In the first case, it has been widely recognized, for example, that the success of IBM's personal computer would have been significantly more difficult to achieve within the constraints of the 'Big Blue' corporate culture. The history of the development of the PC is described at length by Chposky and Leonis [6] who show that the success of the project was only possible by forming an autonomous project team outside the mainstream culture of the company. In their acknowledgements the authors describe their own relationship with IBM in terms that almost defy comprehension.

'... IBM neither endorsed nor authorized the publication of BLUE MAGIC.

'When the text was completed, we submitted a copy to IBM for review. The copy was returned with such marginal comments as "not true" and "conjecture", but in no instance did the company state its version of the points in alleged dispute.'

It is difficult to escape the conclusion that, in terms of the corporate culture of IBM, an opportunity was lost to benefit from the experience of 'Project Chess'.

'This would have been a far different book than it is if IBM had managed to keep key members of the former PC development team on the corporate payroll. These men left the company in disillusionment because they had worked day and night and weekends to make the PC what it was and then the company attempted to fold them back into the IBM bureaucracy with only cursory recognition for what they had accomplished. So they left the company, went elsewhere, made important decisions, earned more money, and built up their estates.'

Many of the more well-publicised examples of radical experiments in organizational structure are in greenfield sites. Nowhere is this more evident than in the case of Jaguar Cars. In the early 1980s the company had drawn back from tackling the serious defects in their working practices, quite understandably placing survival above confronting their industrial relations problems. For this reason, an output quota system was in operation which was strongly reminiscent of the *measured day work* system, which had been at the root of many of the problems encountered by British Leyland in the late 1960s and early 1970s. This is now being attacked vigorously in Jaguar's main plants, following Jaguar's takeover by Ford (Smith [7]).

In their joint venture with GKN (Venture Pressings), however, Jaguar had already introduced many of the working practices so often identified with the Japanese automotive manufacturers. Organization is based on cellular manufacturing principles with cell managers chosen by their colleagues.

Reinforcement of team values has been achieved using outdoor pursuits courses in addition to the more conventional training programme. Recruitment procedures include aptitude testing in addition to a formal interview (Duffy [8]).

Another company with a strong corporate culture, which was seen as an obstacle to change, is General Motors. In the early 1980s the company was, and still is, vulnerable to attack by its competitors, particularly the Japanese. It is perhaps ironical, therefore, that General Motors should seek radical change in their manufacturing systems by means of a joint venture with Toyota. As with the Rank-Toshiba and GEC-Hitachi joint ventures in Britain, the joint venture was entered into by the non-Japanese partner after the failure of a previous enterprise (see Trevor [1]). The General Motors-Toyota joint venture New United Motor Manufacturing Incorporated – known universally by its acronym, NUMMI, was sited at a former General Motors plant at Fremont, California.

As described by Peters [10], the joint venture at NUMMI was driven by a guiding philosophy, consistent with common perceptions of Japanese management procedures, which included:

- '*Kaizen*, the never-ending quest for perfection
- the development of full human potential
- *Jidoka*, the pursuit of superior quality
- build mutual trust
- develop team performance
- every employee as manager
- provide a stable livelihood for all employees.'

The success of NUMMI is widely acknowledged. From a non-viable, wholly-owned plant Fremont became the most efficient plant in General Motors. Output from the joint venture was comparable with the number of cars produced previously by General Motors but with only half of the workforce. What was worrying, however, was that although the same workforce produced both General Motors and Toyota badged cars in the same plant, the customer perception was of the superior quality of the Toyota car. Indeed, in 1990 the market research company J D Power reported that 42% of American new car buyers would not consider a GM product (Feast [11]).

Because of the radical differences between General Motors mainstream corporate culture and NUMMI it is easy to overlook the benefits to Toyota of the NUMMI experience. Tadaaki Jagawa, Director of Production Planning at Toyota, has suggested that NUMMI provided the opportunity to test the just-in-time (JIT) approach to inventory management in an environment remote from their Japanese base. Jagawa described the company's commitment to JIT in the following terms:

'We do not reduce inventory to a minimum for its own sake, but to maintain good production discipline.' (Rodger [12])

It should be noted that the problems encountered by Toyota in the American marketplace are also present in Britain. Trevor and Christie [13] found that British companies were, in general, poorly equipped and lacking in motivation to take advantage of the opportunities of working with Japanese manufacturers.

'In Japan relationships between manufacturers and suppliers are generally closer, more long-term and of greater benefit to both parties than in Britain or the USA. The Japanese see their approach to manufacturer-supplier relations as making a major contribution to competitiveness.' [ibid]).

In contrast to Rank and GEC, who do not appear to have derived any meaningful benefit from their (failed) joint ventures (Trevor [9]), General Motors have incorporated much of their

NUMMI experience into their Saturn project. As with NUMMI, General Motors chose to site the Saturn plant remote from their traditional heartland (Michigan) in Spring Hill, Tennessee, but close to the existing Nissan plant in Smyrna, in the same State.

Although the working practices at Saturn owe much to the experience gained from NUMMI, the organizational structure has not been transplanted uncritically, however, particularly in terms of the general structure of the manufacturing systems. The Japanese motor giants content themselves with the role of final assembly (leading to the frequently expressed complaint that their European and American plants are 'screwdriver' operations). Smooth running of their operations is ensured by close-coupling with their suppliers in terms of unprecedented requirements of quality and delivery. In contrast, the General Motors Saturn plant is a vertically integrated facility in the tradition of the American motor industry, epitomised by Ford's River Rouge plant of 1927. Within its 87 acre plant are facilities covering all stages of production of automobiles, from foundry to final trim.

There is, nevertheless, substantial evidence that the experience gained from NUMMI has been of significant value in the planning of the Saturn plant. This includes:

- Single source suppliers for components and services
- Extremely high stock-turn rates
- 126 receiving stations so that components are delivered at point of use
- Advanced near-net casting processes for engine components.
- Variety of models produced on the same line (eg automatic and manual gearboxes)
- Modular construction based on hang-on thermoplastic body panels on a steel space-frame body skeleton.

(See Feast [11] and Dickson[14]).

Although General Motors have learned a great deal from NUMMI and Saturn, there are some grounds for questioning the extent to which this experience can be transferred into the mainstream businesses. Jane Slaughter, of Labor Notes in Detroit, has suggested that the introduction of team working practices into other General Motors plants has been accompanied by a significant degree of coercion including, but not limited to, the threat of plant closure. She suggests that the team working concept, within General Motors, is based on 'management by stress'.

> 'Given that the team concept is presented as a package, either in a brand new (greenfield) plant or as part of a plan to save the plant from closing, it is difficult for most participants to see that particular aspects are not necessarily part of the team function themselves. Most of both the negative and positive aspects could – in theory, at least – be part of a traditional plant set-up. It is to management's advantage, however, to present the team concept as a package and enforce it that way.'
> (Slaughter [15]).

Slaughter suggests that a different model of the team working concept is practicable, 'although not given the current balance of power.'

James [16] points to the irony that the General Motors joint ventures are proving successful mainly at the expense of their own manufacturing plants.

Management Structure – Devolution Strategies

As has already been suggested, the general trend in the management of manufacturing systems is based on modular management structures. This is, in many respects, inevitable where monolithic, vertically integrated organizations seek to become more responsive to their markets. Under the process which Akio Morita, of Sony, described as '*global localization*', local management is empowered to re-focus their strategic objectives on the needs of their customers and suppliers. The process of globalization has been classified into five stages by Kenichi Ohmae, managing director of McKinsey's Japanese subsidiary (Ohmae [17]). The initial two stages are primarily preparatory and have already been achieved by many Japanese companies. In phase three manufacturing and marketing are given autonomy in key overseas markets. Stage four entails progressive transfer of more intellectually demanding roles such as development, design and research. The final stage is termed 'denationalization' at which point the enterprise is no longer dependent on its national base. There are a number of companies which have long operated on an international basis and, implicitly, are eligible to be considered Ohmae stage five organizations. One company which epitomises this principle is Schlumberger, who have achieved the enviable position that, in extensive market perception surveys, each national group of customers firmly believes that they are dealing with an indigenous company. The French believe that Schlumberger is French; the Germans believe that Schlumberger is German; the Americans believe that Schlumberger is American; etc.

In the modular organization key relationships are much less likely to be dominated by a strong corporate hierarchy. The focus of managerial effort becomes significantly more externalized. Instead of spending a substantial proportion of their time providing (often regular and detailed) reports containing locally useless and abstract data (which is only intelligible for strategic purposes in the context of hierarchically based control systems) senior management within operating units only need to report progress against agreed general strategic and budgetary targets. How they achieve those targets is entirely their own affair.

Following the example of the Japanese automotive and electrical giants, relationships between customers and suppliers have become much more closely coupled. Typical examples of these changes in the nature of customer-supplier relationships include:

- Long-term supply agreements.

- Detailed and demanding delivery requirements.

- Devolution of quality functions to suppliers.

- Arduous quality standards, eg 'zero defects'.

- Single sourcing.

The contractual (or perhaps more appropriately non-contractual) nature of these supply agreements has been the source of considerable criticism among the western competitors to the Japanese enterprises. Japanese government, industry and commerce are linked by old boy networks which put even the British establishment in the shade. For example, a substantial proportion of Japan's senior political figures, and many of its commercial and industrial leaders, were members of the Waseda University Debating Club. Past members are active in the '20th Club' which meets, as its name suggests, on the twentieth day of each month (Thomson [18]). These alliances are semi-formalised in terms of the keiretsu.

One of the most ardent critics of the informal links between Japanese companies has been the American corporate raider T. Boone Pickens. Despite his position as largest shareholder (with a 26% stake) of Koito Manufacturing, a medium-sized Japanese automotive component producer, Pickens was denied a place on the company's board of directors despite the fact that the next largest shareholder Toyota (with 19%) had three representatives. Pickens contended that Toyota were in a position to abuse their membership of the Koito board to impose unfair customer-supplier relationships, in particular forcing price reductions on their suppliers. For their part the company claimed that their denial of a place on the board of directors was due to Pickens's own controversial record and predatory reputation. (See Palmer [19].)

Despite their reservations concerning the apparent anti-competitive contractual and non-contractual relationships, the western competitors have implemented many of the management techniques of the Japanese manufacturers, which a major study of the industry (the International Motor Vehicle Programme at the Massachusetts Institute of Technology-Womack, Jones and Roos [20]) described as the *'lean organization'*. A typical example is the programme of fastener reduction initiated by Ford of Europe in 1986. From their range of 2800 different fasteners Ford set out to eliminate approximately 35% over three years. (See Skinner [21]).

Notwithstanding the trend towards modular manufacturing systems, it is essential to retain the overall viability of the enterprise. If, as suggested by Prahalad and Hamel [4], business units are unwilling, or unable, to take responsibility for their 'core competencies' then a means must be found to:

- Transfer core competencies throughout the operating units

- Highlight generic skill deficiencies within the enterprise.

A company which has anticipated many of the pitfalls described by Prahalad and Hamel is Lucas Industries. Their approach has been described by their managing director, Tony

Gill [22], and by Levi [23]. See Figures 5.1 and 5.2.

The company is organized into seven major subsidiaries, two of which sell into aerospace and industrial systems, with the other five serving the automotive industry but each serving a different sector of this market (fuel injection, braking, electrical equipment and wiring). These primary subsidiaries are further divided into 130 business units. Each operating unit develops its own *competitiveness achievement plan* (CAP), which must be 'credible in its targets and affordable in terms of the resources it requires'. Unusually for British companies (see Goold [3] and KPMG [24]), this plan explicitly requires the business unit to measure its performance against its best international competitor. The business unit is expected to describe in detail how it intends to close the performance gap. Operating units without an acceptable CAP are candidates for disposal or closure.

Although it is of a high priority, and perhaps essential, that operating units should be largely autonomous, it is also imperative that they should not be burdened with unnecessary functional groups. As a consequence, strategies must be developed for providing occasional access to a range of functional specialists whenever a need arises. For the small or medium-sized company this is almost certainly a time of resort to external consultants. For larger technological groups, such as Lucas Industries, such calls for specialist support are likely to occur with some regularity, and there is considerable justification for formalized processes for providing internal consultancy support. Lucas has achieved this by setting up a series of task forces. Although the core of the task force necessarily comprises members of the local workforce, technical specialists may be seconded from other units of the enterprise, for example from a central research and development organization.

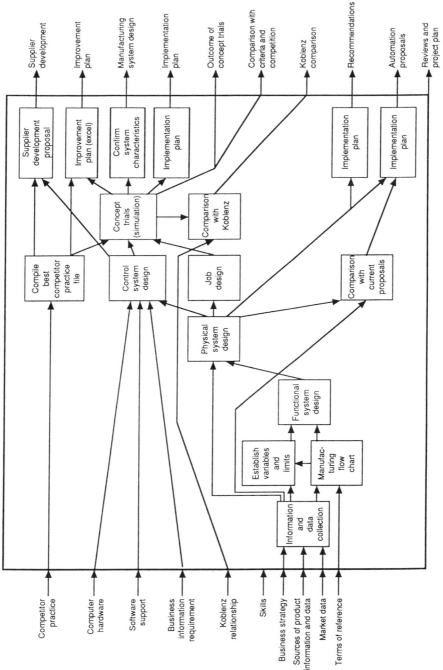

Figure 5-1. SCS Project Plan at Lucas (© IMechE 1986. Reproduced with permission)

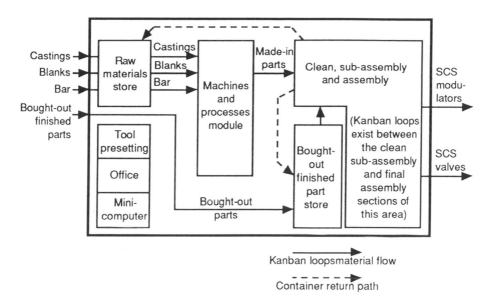

Figure 5-2. SCS Manufacturing Unit at Lucas Girling, Pontypool (© IMechE 1986. Reproduced with permission)

Where Lucas have introduced new approaches to the design and operation of their manufacturing systems they have taken the risky, but potentially rewarding, option of placing the new manufacturing units, as self-contained units, within existing facilities factories within factories. Gill [22] justified this approach in the following terms:

'This was seen as an opportunity, not only to ensure that the manufacturing system would match the best in the world, but also to establish examples of best practice to be copied by other business units within the company.'

As has been described previously, this would be a potentially disastrous approach in a centralized company with a strong corporate culture. Both IBM and General Motors experimented with changes in the organization of their manufacturing systems in manufacturing facilities remote from their corporate heartlands.

Whereas Lucas Industries have maintained and arguably strengthened their corporate research centre, the TI Group have closed their research centre, Hinxton Hall. The strategic reasoning for this action was not financial, as expressed by their chief executive Tony Lewington, in an interview in the Independent newspaper in 1989:

> 'We are in the applied technology not the research business. We spend as much on technology as before but now it is done by the operating companies themselves.
>
> 'Hinxton did half the research for the divisions and the rest for itself. No operating manager believes that work done in the centre is done very well; he also believes he is being overcharged and he also rarely reflects an allocated cost in his pricing.'

This type of strategy is becoming prevalent in the medium sized company. The danger is that the combination of devolution of control to the operating units, which in itself has significant attractions, may combine with undue emphasis on financial performance over strategic objectives (Goold [3]) to erode the core competencies of the enterprise (Prahalad and Hamel [4]). The corporate centre, in devolving control of the planning function to operating units, cannot abnegate the responsibility for maintenance of the strategic viability of the enterprise. In particular, they must take responsibility to highlight generic skill deficiencies within the enterprise and ensure the distribution of core competencies throughout the operating units.

It is becoming increasingly recognized that the influence of the non-executive directors of a company may have an essential role in the provision of benchmarks of corporate competency, since they provide an independent source of expertise and market awareness. Parker [25] draws attention to the problem of lack of commitment of executive directors to the implementation of consultancy recommendations and suggests that the non-executive directors have a key role in the management of change. The constructive utility of non-executive directors in effecting organizational change is also discussed by Marsh [5].

A successful small company which has organized its management according to modular principles is J C Bamford (see Lynn [26]). (Small perhaps in terms of number of employees, approximately 1500, but arguably not in terms of turnover at £328m, a staggering £217k per employee (source April 1989 company report – abstracted in Business, November 1990)). The company is divided into product based teams, each of which has responsibility for all facets of its product from design through to marketing. As with Yamazaki, Bamfords operate in a strongly cyclical market and have seen considerable benefit from remaining in private ownership.

Modular Organization of Production – Group Technology (GT)

In early 1990 SDI Scicon undertook an extensive promotional campaign for its Process Planning and Estimating system SUPERCAPES, '... with Miclass as the integrated Group Technology Classification and Coding element'.

'Group technology is a revolution which is only now in its infancy. In the years to come we expect to see the widespread use of group technology in the UK and throughout the world.' (McKinnon [27]).

The reader could be forgiven for believing that Group Technology was some newly-developed management methodology. Whether Ms McKinnon was ill-informed as to the origins of Group Technology, or chose not to present them, this perception would be wholly erroneous. Indeed, Miclass was well-known among manufacturing systems engineers from the mid 1970s (see Houtzeel [28]). Before examining the history of Group Technology, however, the underlying philosophy will be examined.

Group Technology is presented variously as a philosophy, a strategy and/or a coherent set of management techniques. All are appropriate. The philosophy of Group Technology may be summarized in the following terms:

> *Group Technology seeks to obtain the ECONOMIES OF SCALE OF MASS PRODUCTION IN A BATCH PRODUCTION ENVIRONMENT.*

The strategies and techniques will be discussed at a later stage where the implementation of Computer-Integrated Manufacture (CIM) is considered.

In the introductory remarks of the current work manufacturing systems were presented as evolutionary entities. The most common way in which manufacturing enterprises develop is by expansion. This often entails the transition from jobbing, through small and large batch to mass production, each with differing optimal configurations in terms of production layout, tooling and methods. For example, although Henry Ford developed the model T Ford in 1908, he initially used a (jobbing style) static production methodology and only changed the manufacturing layout to the conveyor system in 1913 (see, for example, Parkinson [29]).

Consider the case of small batch manufacture, i.e. with a correspondingly large numbers of batches. Shopfloor layout would normally be organized on functional lines, i.e. with general-purpose machines performing similar operations grouped together, and with personnel specializing in the operation of a particular machine or class of machines, e.g. 'turners' specializing in the operation of lathes, etc. Because machines are regularly re-set for each batch, few, if any, product-specific jigs and fixtures would be considered necessary. Contrast this with the production environment typical in classical mass production, where the production machinery is tailored to a specific product. Machines may integrate several processes within a single transfer line, with the machining axes and feed rates optimized to that product and tailored to the workflow, often with components pre-set on specialized jigs or pallets. Operatives are largely unskilled with the largely mechanistic, primary role of ensuring smooth flow of products, waste and consumables to and from the machine. In contrast, the staff who set, maintain and service the machines are highly skilled, although they may still retain a strong craft-based demarcation.

By identifying groups of components with similar manufacturing process routes, and corresponding groups of machines which are associated with these product groups, large, functionally-organized factories can be reorganized into modular 'factories within factories', each organized around a single product or group of products. This is the essential feature of the Group Technology philosophy, which is essentially a product-centred approach to batch manufacture.

The consequences for manufacturing organization are many and diverse. There is an opportunity for individual machines to be adapted to manufacture a much more restricted range of products than that for which they were originally designed, for example by simplifying machine set ups and providing specific jigs and fixtures, inspection templates and preset gauges. Staff are likely to be more versatile, in terms of the range of machines which they can use, than in the corresponding functionally organized manufacturing systems, but their skill level on a particular machine is unlikely to match that of a specialist operative in the functional organization. Supervisory staff are likely to be chosen on the basis of their interpersonal skills, rather than their craft background and technical expertise.

The problem which Group Technology addresses is whether or not it is possible to exploit ideas which arise from successful mass production in a batch manufacture environment. Group Technology is often regarded as synonymous to Cellular Manufacturing but there is not a direct equivalence. It is common to find cellular manufacturing organizations based on system design principles which are largely incompatible with Group Technology philosophies, in particular Flexible Manufacturing Systems. Similarly it is possible to devise manufacturing layouts for Group Technology which are not cellular, for example flow lines or, in an extreme case cited by Burbidge[34], jobbing. The assumption of the equivalence of Group Technology and Cellular Manufacturing neglects other important facets of Group Technology including, for example, the needs for design rationalization, the introduction of coding and classification systems and the development of new working methods.

Isolated examples of Group Technology were developed by imaginative managers from the beginning of the twentieth century (although not described by this name) but without the techniques gaining widespread popularity. As is by no means uncommon in the history of manufacturing systems it was only when Group Technology was the only viable solution that it was developed systematically. Again, as is by no means unusual, it was developed in isolation, in the USSR in the late 1940s and early 1950s, by a number of engineers, although it became known in the west from the writings of Mitrofanov [30].

Although they had experimented with Group Technology in the pre-war years the main developments in Group Technology took place in the immediate post-war period. The problems confronting the USSR were that the World War (and Stalin's ideologically-based industrial policies) had left it with serious labour shortages, a ravaged industrial base and an urgent need to expand production. Furthermore, industrial production of war materials almost invariably demands a substantial proportion of techniques derived from mass production. Politically and economically the USSR could be best described as centralist and autocratic, with industrial managers appointed on the basis of their party loyalty rather than their managerial talents. (For the history of Group Technology in the USSR, see Grayson [31]).

There is a strong case for the viewpoint that the potential for Group Technology, based on the Soviet research, was recognized first in the UK in Manchester by John Burbidge [32-34] and by Edwards and his associates (Edwards [35]), and in Birmingham by Gallagher (Gallagher and Knight [36,37]) and Grayson, the translator of Mitrofanov's book.

In the UK GT was introduced into a number of companies with spectacular success. Figures quoted by Edwards [35] for Serck Audco, a manufacturer of valves, include:

- 67% increase in sales volume

- 46% stock reduction

- Stock/sales ratio reduced by 28%

- Throughput time reduced from 12 to 5 weeks on average

- Dispatches per employee up 83%

- Average earnings increased by 63%.

The success of Group Technology in these companies, coupled with a lack of industrial awareness and critical analysis, led to a perception that GT was a universal solution to the structural defects of British manufacturing – in short a panacea. Substantial government support was provided for the introduction of GT, including the establishment of a GT support centre (see NEDO [38-40]). As is so often the case, GT became a successful solution in search of new problems – to which there is no guarantee of success. Perhaps inevitably, the spectacular successes were followed by equally dramatic failures. The mood was best captured in 1977 by two former researchers into GT,

Ray Leonard and Keith Rathmill [41], who analyzed 'the Group Technology Myths'. This work was deficient in the appreciation of the need for organizational change, taking the classical hierarchy, and the job functions within it, as both axiomatic and immutable. There is no doubt, however, that it reflected the mood of the times with a general antipathy to GT, so much so that, although John Burbidge [33] was to publish a well argued rebuttal entitled 'Whatever happened to GT?', the concept of GT was widely discredited.

In the rest of the world, and particularly the USA, Germany and Japan, manufacturing systems designers developed GT later and with the benefit of the British experience (both positive and negative). Gallagher and Knight [37] suggest that the Leonard and Rathmill's criticism has proved unfounded:

'There is no doubt that the test of time and the actual implementation of many cells in recent years, particularly in the USA, have rejected this criticism.' (ibid. page 16).

This section began by criticizing Lindsay McKinnon of SDI Scicon for failing to draw attention to the long history of Group Technology. This is perhaps a little unfair, since proponents of GT (including the author) in the UK have had an uphill struggle to reinstate GT after the failures of the mid 1970s. It is extremely important to recognize that:

- GT is not a new introduction
- that it has been developed to a considerable level of sophistication since its early failures
- that it is becoming more, rather than less, relevant with reduction in product life cycles and the increasing variety of generically similar products.

Where McKinnon concurs with previous writers, even with

Leonard and Rathmill[41], is, firstly, her recognition that purchase costs of proprietary systems are small relative to the implementation costs. Secondly, the level of management ability required for successful implementation is high. Last, but not least, she emphasizes the essential needs for total commitment *and involvement* of senior management.

Modular Organization of Production – Flexible Manufacturing Systems

As has been mentioned, GT is not the only strategy which is largely (although not exclusively) based on cellular manufacturing principles. Flexible Manufacturing Systems (FMS) are also commonly cellular in their organization. A number of authors have gone so far as to suggest that Flexible Manufacturing Systems are a logical progression from, and hence a replacement for, Group Technology systems. As will be shown, nothing could be further from the truth.

The fundamental objective of FMS is often expressed in terms of the 'batch size of one', i.e. it should be no more expensive, per component, to produce a single component than it is to produce thousands. The primary variable elements in the computation of economic batch quantity (EBQ) are the set-up cost per component, which decreases inversely with batch size, and the inventory holding costs, which are directly proportional to batch size. Thus, for the EBQ to be insensitive to volume, set-up costs should be (ideally) zero and inventory should be minimized. However, whereas GT minimizes the effects of set-up costs by grouping batches of components with common, or near common, manufacturing process routes, Flexible Manufacturing Systems use sophisticated and versatile machines which require minimal setting up, for example often changing (and gauging) subsequent tools from a carousel while the current tool is cutting. Such machines defy classification according to traditional craft demarcations (lathes, milling machines, etc.) and are commonly described as 'Machining Centres'.

Thus Flexible Manufacturing Systems are the antithesis of Group Technology. The idea of scheduling batches with similar set-ups and the provision of special jigs, fixtures, gauges, etc., is anathema to the Flexible Manufacturing Systems approach.

FMS is principally proposed as a solution for problems with:

- Variable batch sizes

- Unpredictable order profiles

- High product obsolescence

- Historically high work-in-progress

- Complex parts.

It is particularly appropriate in a small batch subcontracting organization, where companies have no access to such data as market forecasts or product development plans (particularly where alternative production processes are possible) and serve a number of customers.

In many ways the two philosophies are complementary, with those components which cannot be incorporated into GT cells being candidates for flexible cells. For example, Ferranti, one of the pioneers of GT in Britain, found (in 1969) that 60% of their workload was suitable for Group Technology manufacturing systems. It follows that the remaining 40% was sufficiently different in its manufacturing process routes, or its demand predictability, or its volume or planning horizon, that Group Technology rationalization was not achievable. This is consequently a natural candidate for a Flexible Manufacturing Systems approach.

In many respects the history of Flexible Manufacturing Systems in the UK mirrors that of Group Technology. D T N Williamson, one of the few British engineers to have been elected a member of the Royal Society, was responsible for developing

'System 24' – one of the design aims was that it should run for 24 hours per day – at Molins, the tobacco machinery company, in the 1960s. (See, for example, Williamson [42]). This is credited by Brian Small [43], of Ingersoll Engineers, as the first FMS (perhaps competing with Sunstrand Automation for the title). Despite having the early experience, or perhaps because of it, an opportunity was wasted to capitalize on the potential advantage of being first in the field.

As has been suggested, there is often little or no distinction made between different forms of Cellular Manufacturing Systems. Figures 5.3 and 5.4 show the experience of a cross sample of British companies which show a clear trend to the adoption of Cellular Manufacturing Systems, with the benefits already apparent.

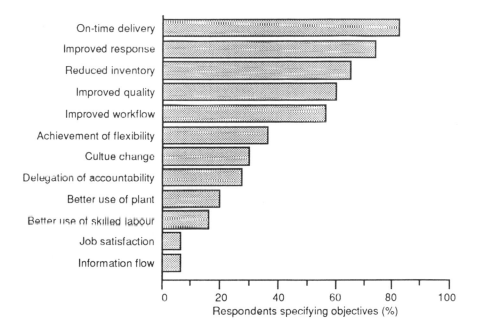

Figure 5-3. Main Objectives of Cell Introduction (© **Ingersoll Engineers Ltd. Reproduced with permission)**

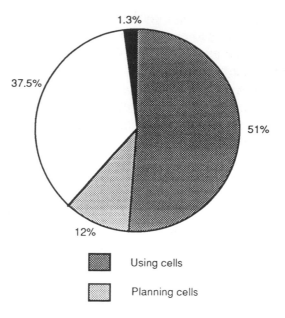

Figure 5-4. Use of Cells in UK Engineering Industry (© **Ingersoll Engineers Ltd. Reproduced with permission)**

Modular Middle Management – the Missing Tier

As has been described, the prevailing trend, in both the organization of the corporate structure and its manufacturing systems, is towards a product-oriented modular form. It is by no means unusual, however, for the senior levels of management within individual business units to retain a functionally-based structure. If such a situation is perpetuated it is likely to undermine any of the intended benefits of changing to a product-centred organization.

Such staff are likely to be experienced, and arguably accomplished, within their restricted domains. They may be reluctant to test their managerial skills in an unfamiliar role.

They are, in all probability, settled and rather set in their ways, mature – perhaps near to retirement – and will be inclined, albeit passively (see Scase and Goffee [44]), to resist change unless it is of demonstrable personal benefit.

At first sight the most attractive option would be the one adopted by a large number of companies, to institute voluntary redundancy or early retirement programmes. The latter course has often been an attractive option because of the large surpluses which have accrued in many company pension schemes, to which the companies may not have direct access but may use for qualifying purposes within a more comprehensive reorganization. Where necessary, new (usually younger) staff, who don't have the preconceptions and prejudices of the incumbent staff, may be brought into the business. This approach has serious risks, however. In many organizations the operating procedures are minimally documented. Where it is maintained, the company's documentation of their management practices often gives only an extremely approximate reflection of reality, being deficient in some areas, contradictory in others and in some cases completely wrong. The existing management are likely to have a deep and potentially valuable understanding of these informal aspects of the operation of the enterprise. In addition, although their views are probably jaundiced by years of corporate neglect, particularly in terms of training (see Constable and McCormick [45], Handy [46] and Clutterbuck and Crainer [47]), there is often a strong underlying loyalty to the company.

There is considerable merit, therefore, in exploiting the specialist experience and loyalty of the existing senior management within the business units. However, because of the transition to a more product-centred organization, their managerial role within the enterprise must necessarily change. Where the corporate restructuring is carefully planned, many of these problems will be tackled in the process of reorganization. The options, which are not necessarily exclusive, are

- To integrate the functional specialist into the product-centred organization

- To increase the degree of specialism so that the functional manager can become an internal consultant.

In either case, the manager is likely to view developments with some trepidation since issues of loss of status, the pressures of adapting to a new role and of learning to work with a new set of colleagues must be addressed.

The topical description of the second role is the *'Technological Gatekeeper'*.

'Individuals chosen as sources or potential sources of technical information are often the same individuals identified as the sources of the best technical ideas by their co-workers. ... Persons combining the attributes of internal discussion partners and sources of the best technical ideas who also have the greater technical contacts outside the research and development laboratory have been defined as technological gatekeepers.' (Taylor [48]).

The statistics on training suggest that many middle managers are likely to be poorly equipped to return to a purely technical role. (See, for example, TSA [49]). Indeed, it is questionable whether the average level of training expenditure is sufficient to equip any manager for a significant change in operational responsibilities. Furthermore, the averages conceal a small proportion of companies devoting a substantial fraction of their turnover to training while the overwhelming majority have relied on the recruitment of staff who have received their training elsewhere. This was acknowledged by Paul Foden, management services director of ERF, in the following terms:

'After 1983 there was a lack of people coming through into skilled jobs and we had to go out into the market to get people who had been trained by other companies, like Rolls-Royce. They brought their vices with them.'

ERF is a good example of the survival of a small and threatened family business, in an industry of giants, by the means of a well-defined corporate strategy. Their Group Technology-based approach replaced a product range based on a huge variety of options of engines, transmissions and axles, with a modular range based on Cummins engines, Eaton transmissions and Rockwell axles.

Whether a functional specialist is to become a product-centred manager or to become more specialized, it is highly likely that he or she has spent a substantial proportion of recent managerial activity in a short-term reactive role, often described as 'fire-fighting'. This is particularly true in the common case where change in manufacturing systems is triggered by an obvious management crisis. The manager will, in all probability, have had very little time, energy or inclination to keep up-to-date in the technology of the product, its methods of manufacture or relevant developments in manufacturing management. It is a truism that the most effective training programmes are those which individual employees can recognize as being of direct relevance to their operating role. As a consequence it is of prime importance that the enterprise should develop a training programme which covers the following aspects of the enterprise:

- Familiarization with the company's product ranges, its manufacturing processes and its operating procedures

- Familiarization with the marketplace, in particular the product ranges and marketing strategies of competitors

- Familiarization with the technology of the product, particularly in terms of current manufacturing processes and competing technologies, the organization of manufacturing systems and corporate strategy.

In many respects this programme merely summarizes what a large proportion of successful companies do as a matter of course, in particular the key Japanese enterprises. These activities can be undertaken at a number of levels, from day-to-day operational activities to the strategic level. For each manager a tailored programme of activities should be devised between the manager and his or her senior colleagues. This may include (but should not be restricted to):

- Visits to customers

- Attendance at equipment exhibitions and trade fairs

- Visits to identified best practitioners (such visits are organized regularly by government agencies, trade associations and professional societies)

- Short courses

- Courses of significant duration, e.g. MSc taught courses

Where a factory-within-a-factory approach is taken (as used by Lucas – see Gill [22]), as many managers as possible should be aware of the learning process derived from the implementation.

The development of technological gatekeepers is likely to prove an effective solution to the problems anticipated by Prahalad and Hamel [4], i.e. the erosion of the core competencies of the enterprise. The key question is the identification of those managers who would be most suitable to act as 'guinea pigs' to introduce the concept to the enterprise. As described by Prietula and Simon [50], the 'experts in your midst' are not necessarily those in the positions of executive responsibility but are, in general, well-known to their colleagues and can be identified by peer esteem surveys. Once their commitment is obtained, they will be powerful advocates among their fellow employees.

Management Philosophy

As was suggested earlier, there is no one right answer as to the correct organizational structure of an enterprise. It depends on company history, markets, the nature of the manufacturing processes and many other variables. Returning, once again, to the views of Drucker [51]:

'Anyone with experience in management knows a healthy organization structure when he sees it (which is seldom enough). But he is like a doctor who knows a healthy person when he sees one but can only define 'health' negatively, that is, as the absence of disease, deformity or pathological degeneration.

'Similarly, a healthy organization is hard to describe. But the symptoms of malorganisation can be identified. Whenever they are present there is need for thorough examination of the organization structure. Whenever they are present the right structural principles are not being observed.'

The same is true for the techniques of management. The particular methods in use at any one time result from a general consensus of best practice rather than any fundamental scientific basis. Such consensus is difficult to achieve throughout an enterprise, in particular across the range of functional groups. It is by no means uncommon for strategic changes to be resisted effectively by a particular functional group, despite their general acceptance throughout the rest of the organization. Though often portrayed as Luddites, the opposers of the change may perceive – correctly or incorrectly – insurmountable difficulties in its implementation.

In the current section two topics will be discussed where fundamental changes in the organization of manufacture have been enabled because a consensus has been reached as to the importance of a particular strategic objective. In the first case, that of Just-In-Time (JIT), a long-term strategic priority of the financial specialists of the enterprise, the minimization of inventories for financial reasons, has been realized because production management recognized entirely different justifications for 'lean production'. In the second case, Total Quality Control, general perceptions of Quality Assurance as an adverse cost, and that quality procedures are disruptive to good production management, led to an anti-quality culture in many companies. The work of Crosby [52], in particular, and the Japanese obsession with quality, in general, has led to the reappraisal of the significance of the maintenance of challenging levels of quality assurance. (See also Oakland [53]).

There are essentially two levels of resistance to change. At the passive level, staff are unlikely to commit themselves fully to the projects where they discern no personal benefit. However they are not generally disposed to frustrate the project deliberately unless they have a grudge against the organization for other reasons – a situation which is by no means unusual. Active resistance is likely to occur where a functional group believes that an organizational change will be prejudicial to their interests.

One of the recurring themes of the current work is that management change very often only occurs under extreme duress. As Dr Johnson said: 'Depend on it, Sir, when a man knows he is to be hanged in a fortnight, it concentrates his mind wonderfully'. Taiichi Ohno (originator of the Toyota Production System) expressed the same sentiment rather more coarsely as 'the last fart of the ferret', referring to the pungent scent given out by the animal when threatened (more usually associated with the skunk), indicating that he believed that his subordinates were most creative, and productive, when placed under extremes of pressure.

Friction between accountants and engineers occurs in many

companies and often impedes progress. The Japanese are usually – and as will be seen, inaccurately – regarded as being immune to such industrial discord and, consequently, the example given here is from Toyota. Although Ohno is associated in the minds of many with Toyota and the Toyota Production System (see Shingo [54]), he left the company after an unsuccessful battle against what eventually became the NUMMI joint venture project (with General Motors). His adversary, Masaya Hanai, was a financial specialist who believed that a partnership with an American firm would smooth the way for Toyota to enter the United States market. Ohno, for his part, did not wish to give the Americans any knowledge about the Toyota Production System. Matters came to a head in September 1978, when Hanai was promoted to Chairman and Ohno was voted off the board – so much for the much-vaunted consensus management of the Japanese. (For further commentary see Shinohara [55]).

Just-In-Time (JIT)

The case for reduction in stocks appears unanswerable. It potentially releases capital for other purposes, allows personnel to be re-deployed to value-adding activities, reduces the complexity of production control (by reducing the number of components or batches which must be kept in active files), removes clutter due to inter-operation storage from the shopfloor and eliminates the need for large scale raw material and finished goods storage facilities.

The scale of the problem may be appreciated through the following example. Sheffield Forgemasters was a company in serious financial difficulties when Philip Wright joined as Chief Executive in 1985. As was by no means unusual with companies in management difficulties, there was obviously a large amount of work-in-progress. He asked his staff for their own assessment of the quantity, with their best guess being 500 tonnes. His own estimate was 10000 tonnes. When accurately calculated it transpired that there was a total of 30000 tonnes of stock. (For further description of Wright's transformation of Sheffield Forgemasters, see van de Vliet [56]).

It is reasonable to ask, therefore, why such high levels of inventory have been tolerated for so long. In the first instance, opportunity costs (for example the costs of choosing not to reorganize manufacturing systems) are not commonly quantified. Secondly, inability to provide service to those further down the supply chain, and ultimately the customer, is a much more visible failure than the creeping inefficiencies of maintaining excess stocks. Thus:

- Raw material stores keep (usually extremely generous) safety stocks to ensure that production is not delayed.

- Manufacturing relies on inter-operation storage to ensure a steady flow through production facilities, with the added bonus that there is always likely to be a batch near completion if an urgent customer order is received.

- Finished goods stores are packed to the doors to ensure that no request, however unreasonable, from customers or stockholders, is left unfulfilled.

This is referred to as the 'Just-In-Case' approach to manufacturing systems management.

The high priests of this cult of inventory are the progress chasers or, to use their alternative title, the expediters. Nominally, at least, they occupy a position near the bottom of the organization's family tree. Their power is one of consensus, which comes from the general perception that they ensure that customers receive their orders expeditiously through their intervention. Welcome in every office, from the production controller to the managing director, the expediter is constantly seeking the necessary authority to vary the production schedule.

The effect on the management of manufacturing systems is pernicious:

- Job tickets may be manually changed without the production schedule being updated.

- Machine set-ups may be changed, even part of the way through a batch, to rush an urgent order through.

- Tooling is unlikely to be available when required.

- Batches are unlikely to be where the schedule indicates that they should be, resulting in considerable time being spent locating missing batches.

- Products may be released into production with shortages, in the hope that the deficiencies can be corrected before final assembly.

- Scrap and rework will be assigned extremely low priorities, leading to a proliferation of what is effectively useless material being kept on the shop-floor.

These practices are both contagious and habit-forming. If they are allowed to take hold, the whole organization becomes subverted, being preoccupied with serving the customer who shouts the loudest. Customers who do not complain are extremely unlikely ever to receive their orders. Eventually, all that the progress chasers are doing is working against each other to ensure that 'their' customer obtains preferential treatment. Ultimately, the system will fail even the criterion which was the objective for its establishment in the first place, that of ensuring that customers receive their orders when promised. Thus practices which were started for the best of motives are likely to undermine the competitiveness of the entire enterprise.

The symptoms of the malaise are obvious. Layers of dust (or

even of rust!) on components are an immediate give-away of how long they have been languishing on the shopfloor. Damaged, altered or missing job tickets are indicative of the insidious activities of the progress chaser. It isn't necessary to be particularly clever, or even experienced, to spot the signs, but it is absolutely essential to be objective. Philip Wright, of Sheffield Forgemasters, described how his experience with PA Consultants equipped him for recognising these signs:

> 'The PA training teaches you to smell if it's a good business, whatever the company actually makes.'

So the problem addressed by Taiichi Ohno, in devising the Just-In-Time philosophy at Toyota was well-known, and it would be naive to believe that his solution was either unique or original. What Ohno possessed was the personal commitment, insight and, above all, ruthlessness, to turn his analysis into a working system. A further crucial asset was the commitment of support by the Toyoda family.

The basic principle of Just-In-Time is trivial, that individual components and, where necessary, production equipment and instructions, should arrive at a given work-station (including goods-inward and despatch) at the moment the previous assignment is completed. The logistic problems are intimidating, however, since a large number of events must be scheduled simultaneously with no margin for error.

Total Quality Control

The second major aspect of the management of manufacturing systems which the Japanese have placed firmly on the corporate agenda is that of quality and its management. As with Just-In-Time, there is nothing mystical, or even particularly original, about Japanese analysis of quality. As described by Imai

[57], the Japanese acknowledge their debt to American mentors, in particular Deming and Juran, the latter providing a link to the pioneering work of Elton Mayo, through his work at Western Electric.

As has been described, traditional Just-In-Case type manufacturing systems are tolerant of significant degrees of inferior quality goods. Where a large proportion of shopfloor space is devoted to the storage of large quantities of part-finished components, much of the work-in-progress will contain incompletely kitted assemblies, batches awaiting inspection and rejects awaiting disposal. In Just-In-Time systems, however, this space just simply isn't available. Furthermore, if components of unacceptable quality are delivered into JIT systems, then production is liable to be halted immediately, since there is no provision for safety stocks in pure JIT systems. As a consequence, JIT systems are extremely intolerant of inferior quality components or production technology.

Total Quality Control has many facets. Firstly, quality is designed into products. This ensures, perhaps paradoxically, that a minimum of inspection is required. Secondly, the workforce is educated, empowered and motivated to think quality, which eliminates the need for the employment of specialist inspection personnel. Thirdly, a wide variety of scientific methods, for example Statistical Process Control are used to monitor and control manufacturing processes. Mikio Shoji [58], of Kajima Corporation, described his company's approach to Total Quality Control as the elimination of *mudu* – uneconomy, *muri* – unreasonable, and *mura* – uneven. In short, truths which are available to any western manager, simply by using his/her common sense. What would be unfamiliar to the western manager, however, is the obsessive zeal with which these simple goals are pursued.

There is an increasing trend for the acceptance of the conspiracy theory of Japanese ascendancy in manufacturing, of which the texts by James [16] and Choate [59] are typical. There is much to be said for the old adage that one should never attribute to corruption that which can be explained by incompetence. However devious and underhand the Japanese may, or may not, have been in gaining market advantage (whether by protection of their home markets by tariffs and other protectionist devices, by dumping into markets and other unfair competitive practices), they have been assisted, beyond their wildest dreams, by the naiveté of the regulatory agencies, by insane fiscal policies which penalize investment in manufacturing systems, by the complacency of indigenous manufacturers (relying on chauvinism and xenophobia as marketing strategies – rather than price, quality and delivery) and by the willingness of consumers to believe their (occasionally dubious) claims concerning the technical merit and quality of their products.

To take one simple example, one of Britain's automotive component suppliers was an enthusiastic proponent of Statistical Process Control to ensure the quality of their products. They found their customers not only indifferent to the merits of this methodology, but also resentful of the additional costs which they believed the methods incurred. SPC was therefore discontinued until the customers observed the insistence of Japanese manufacturers on Total Quality Control.

Implications for Customer-Supplier Relationships – Managing the Supply Chain

From the preceding discussion it should be realized that it is extremely difficult, perhaps impossible, to implement Just-In-Time and Total Quality Control programmes without there being a significant impact on both suppliers and customers. In the 'lean organization', where inventory minimization and high throughput are of the utmost importance, both the dissipation of management effort and allocation of space for inspection activities is anathema. The lean organization concentrates exclusively on a relatively narrow range of value-adding operations. In such circumstances bought-out raw materials, components and sub-assemblies must be of perfect quality, at the supply end, and effort in rework and post-delivery restitution must also be ruthlessly eliminated at the customer end.

Schonberger [60] suggests that unnecessary automation represents a lost opportunity for quality attainment. Workers who are involved, and understand the processes, will identify with quality objectives:

'If the plant is very large, managers should try to carve it into factories within the factory, semi-self-contained units, with each focusing on one component or on a narrow family of components. They should also look for ways to change from a single high-capacity production line to multiple slower ones. Each will be simpler to control, simpler to maintain, and more product-focused. Each small line or cell can focus on a separate set of subcustomers. This is in keeping with the potent 'new' concept that everyone has a customer – the next process – and that satisfying the needs of that customer should take top priority.'

Attainment of Just-In-Time and Total Quality Control accordingly requires the formation of a modular internal economy. At the periphery of this system are the procurement and despatch functions. A natural priority of the procurement function is the assurance of reliable supplier performance. As a consequence, it has become common practice for large companies with a need for a broad range of simple bought-in components to seek to enhance the capability of their suppliers. This includes, but is not necessarily restricted to, the following actions:

• Devolution of quality conformance authority to suppliers.

- Technical support to suppliers
- Guidance on training
- Assistance in evaluation of new production technology
- Guarantees to maintain preferred supplier status – subject to attainment of prescibed quality standards
- Financial assistance for investment programmes.

The benefits to suppliers are considerable. Attainment of preferred or exclusive supplier status, with typically a three year guarantee of continuity of procurement, enables companies who have been reluctant to invest in new production technology to purchase more reliable machinery which, in its turn, leads to further quality improvements.

Although there are undoubtedly significant benefits for the suppliers, the motives for these actions are far from altruistic. In exchange for their advice and assistance the customers reduce their internal quality assurance costs, ideally eliminating inwards goods inspection, and reduce the need for carrying safety stocks to allow for shortages caused by high rejection rates. In addition the Japanese giants have established the practice of building efficiency factors into the long-term supply contracts, whereby the component price reduces steadily in real terms throughout the lifetime of the contract. (Schonberger [61,62]).

The natural corollary to award of preferred or exclusive supplier status is that the number of suppliers for any one enterprise is likely to reduce dramatically. In the European automotive industry, for example, the companies with minimal supply chains have as few as 200 suppliers, whilst the traditional enterprises may have as many as 5000.

References

[1] Roethlisberger, F. and Dickson, W., "Management and the Worker", *Harvard University Press*, Cambridge, MA 1939.

[2] Kanter, R. M., *When Giants Learn to Dance: Mastering the Challenge of Strategy, Management and Careers in the 1990s*, Simon and Schuster, New York 1989.

[3] Goold M. (with Quinn, J. J.), *Strategic Control: Milestones for Long-term Performance*, The Economist Books/Hutchinson, London 1990.

[4] Prahalad, C. K. and Hamel, G., "The Core Competence of the Corporation", *Harvard Business Review*, May-June 1990, pp79-91.

[5] Marsh, P., *Short-termism on Trial*, Institutional Fund Manager's Association, London 1990.

[6] Chposky, J. and Leonis, T., *Blue Magic: The People, Power and Politics Behind the IBM Personal Computer*, Grafton, New York 1988.

[7] Smith, M., "Jaguar bares its teeth at outmoded work practices", *Financial Times*, October 11 1990.

[8] Duffy, H., "Pressing need for new ideas", *Financial Times*, October 25, 1990.

[9] Trevor, M., *Toshiba's New British Company: Competitiveness through Innovation in Industry*, Policy Studies Institute, London 1988.

[10] Peters, T., *Thriving on Chaos: Handbook for a Management Revolution*, Macmillan, London 1987.

[11] Feast, R., "A Mission to Convert Buyers", *Financial Times Survey: World Car Industry*, September 18 1990.

[12] Rodger, I., "Delivering tomorrow orders made today", *Financial Times*, September 10 1990.

[13] Trevor, M. and Christie, I., *Manufacturers and Suppliers in Britain and Japan*, Policy Studies Institute, London 1988.

[14] Dickson, M., "The Workers Tell it the Way they see it", *Financial Times*, November 8, 1990.

[15] Slaughter, J., "The Team Concept in the US Auto Industry: Implications for Unions", Conference on the Japanization of British Industry, Editor N Oliver, Cardiff Business School, September 17-18, 1987.

[16] James, B. G., *Trojan Horse: The Ultimate Japanese Challenge to Western Industry*, W H Allen-Mercury, London 1989.

[17] Ohmae, K., *The Borderless World: Power and Strategy in the Interlinked Economy*, Collins, New York 1990.

[18] Thomson, R., "Debating club where members prefer the nod and the wink", *Financial Times*, January 30 1990.

[19] Palmer, G., "Shoot-out at the Koito Corral", *Business*, November 1990, 92-96.

[20] Womack, J. P., Jones, D. T. and Roos, D., *The Machine That Changed The World*, Rawson Associates, New York 1990.

[21] Skinner, N. H., "Ford Reduces Fastener Inventories to Cut Costs", *Chartered Mechanical Engineer*, November 1986, 37-40.

[22] Gill, A. K., Engineers Matter – "The Lucas Key to International Success", *Proceedings of the Institution of Mechanical Engineers*, Series B, 1986, 205-213.

[23] Levi, J., "Prince of Darkness Sees the Light", *Business*, September 1990, 81-86.

[24] *Information for Strategic Management: A Survey of Leading Companies 1990*, KPMG Peat Marwick Management Consultants, 1990.

[25] Parker, H., "Outsiders come Inside", *Management Today*, October 1989, 131-138.

[26] Lynn, M., "Digging for Victory", *Business*, October 1990, 112-115.

[27] McKinnon, L., *SUPERCAPES/Miclass Group Technology: Its Benefits and Cost Saving*, SDI Scicon, London 1990.

[28] Houtzeel, A., "Miclass, a Classification System based on Group Technology", Society of Manufacturing Engineers, paper MS75-721, 1975.

[29] Parkinson, C. N., *Big Business*, Weidenfeld and Nicolson, London 1974.

[30] Mitrofanov, S. P., *Scientific Principles of Group Technology*, British Library Lending Division Translation, 1966.

[31] Grayson, T. J., "Group Technology in the USSR: Conditions and Prospects", *Chartered Mechanical Engineer*, July 1981, pp26-30.

[32] Burbidge, J. L., *The Introduction of Group Technology*, Heinemann, London 1975.

[33] Burbidge, J. L., "Whatever Happened to GT?" *Management Today*, September 1978, pp87-89 and 193.

[34] Burbidge, J. L., *Group Technology in the Engineering Industry*, Mechanical Engineering Publications, London 1979.

[35] Edwards, G. A. B., *Readings in Group Technology*, Machinery Publishing Co, Brighton, England 1971.

[36] Gallagher, C. C. and Knight, W. A., *Group Technology*, Butterworth, London 1973.

[37] Gallagher, C. C. and Knight, W. A., *Group Technology Production Methods in Manufacture*, Ellis Horwood, Chichester, England 1986.

[38] *Production Planning and Control*, National Economic Development Office, London 1966.

[39] *Better Delivery*, National Economic Development Office, London 1969.

[40] *Why Group Technology*, National Economic Development Office, London 1975.

[41] Leonard, R. and Rathmill, K., "The Group Technology Myths", *Management Today*, January 1977 66-69.

[42] Williamson, D. T. N., "The Pattern of Batch Manufacture and its Influence on Machine Tool Design", *Proceedings of the Institution of Mechanical Engineers*, 182, 1968, 870-895.

[43] Small, B. W., "Wealth Generation – Our Essential Task", *Proceedings of the Institution of Mechanical Engineers*, 197B, 1983, 131-141

[44] Scase, R. and Goffee, R., *Reluctant Managers: Their Work and Lifestyles*, Unwin-Hyman, London 1989

[45] Constable, J. and McCormick, R., *The Making of British Managers*: Report to the British Institute of Management and the Confederation of British Industry into Management Training, Education and Development, British Institute of Management, 1987.

[46] Handy, C., *The Making of Managers*: a Report on Management Education, Training and Development in the USA, West Germany, France, Japan and the UK, National Economic Development Office, London, 1987.

[47] Clutterbuck, D. and Crainer, S., *The Decline and Rise of British Industry*, W H Allen-Mercury, London 1988.

[48] Taylor, R. L., "The Impact of Organizational Change on the Technological Gatekeeper Role", *IEEE Transactions on Engineering Management*, EM-33(1), February 1986, pp12-16.

[49] *Training in Britain*, Training Services Agency, Her Majesty's Stationery Office, London 1989.

[50] Prietula, M. J. and Simon, H. A., "The Experts in Your Midst", *Harvard Business Review*, January-February 1989, 120-124.

[51] Drucker, P. F., The Practice of Management, Mercury London, 1955.

[52] Crosby, P. B., *Quality is Free*, McGraw-Hill, New York 1979.

[53] Oakland, J. S., *Total Quality Management*, Heinemann, 1989.

[54] Shingo, S., *Study of 'Toyota' Production System from Industrial Engineering Viewpoint*, Japan Management Association, Tokyo 1981.

[55] Shinohara, I., *NPS New Production System: JIT Crossing Industry Boundaries*, Toyo Keizai Shinposha, Tokyo, 1985 (English Translation: Productivity Press, Cambridge MA 1988).

[56] Van de Vliet, A., "Out of the Furnace", *Management Today*, January 1990 50-55.

[57] Imai, M., *Kaizen: The Key to Japan's Competitive Success*, Random House, New York 1986.

[58] Shoji, M., "Without Muda, Muri, Mura", *Mechanical Engineering*, January 1988, 41.

[59] Choate, P., *Agents of Influence*, Hutchinson, London 1990.

[60] Schonberger, R. J., "Frugal manufacturing", *Harvard Business Review*, September-October 1987, pp95-100.

[61] Schonberger, R. J., *World Manufacturing Casebook: Implementing JIT and TQC*, The Free Press, New York 1987.

[62] Schonberger, R. J., *Building a Chain of Customers: Linking Business Functions to Create the World Class Company*, Hutchinson Business Books, London 1990.

6

Financial Aspects of Managing Change in Manufacturing Systems

A recurring theme in engineering management is the inherent bias of financial criteria against the introduction of innovative developments in manufacturing systems, both for day-to-day management and for capital investment.

In the ensuing discussion, it will be shown that there has been a divergence between the accounting tools used by management and the business needs for financial monitoring and control. There has, in consequence, been a gradual atrophy of managerial capability to maintain competitiveness where new enterprises begin operation without this straightjacket of established accountancy methods.

Two key problems will be discussed. Firstly, the effects of existing *production costing systems* on business competitiveness will be considered. This relies, to a great extent, on the published work of Kaplan [1,2] and Johnson and Kaplan [3]. Subsequently, the bias of *investment appraisal methodologies*, against the introduction of Advanced Manufacturing Technology and new methods of managing Manufacturing Systems will be investigated. Once again, a considerable debt is owed to Kaplan [2].

In the final part of the chapter, some strategies will be discussed whereby companies may be able to finance the changes needed in their organizations without making control of their business plans subject to the risks of external finance.

Costing Systems for Management of Manufacturing Systems

Johnson and Kaplan [3], in a comprehensive study of the evolution of accounting practice in business, remark that all of the management accounting practices currently in use had been effectively developed by 1925 (op cit p125). What has changed in the intervening period is the use to which the information contained in the accounting data has been put. In particular, the context in which the information has been used has changed. Whereas the developers of the costing systems maintained a link between accounting data and the underlying operating procedures and processes, based on their own experience, latterly the data has become the largely abstract inputs to abstract control processes – what Johnson and Kaplan call management by numbers.

As has already been suggested, many businesses have little idea of the contribution to profits across their ranges of products. Contribution comprises two elements: firstly, the management of the business must be aware of the costs in manufacturing their products; secondly, they must be aware of the revenues. In many enterprises there is very little evidence that the management has any clear idea of either.

Why have poor accountancy practices perpetuated? The answer, as so often in engineering management, lies in the uncritical adherence to tried and tested, and above all familiar, methods of production costing, long after they have lost their relevance and effectiveness. Traditional cost accounting practices were developed at a time of relatively low rates of mechanization, with a correspondingly large proportion of product costs, typically in excess of 60%, being due to direct labour costs. In manufacturing systems where there was a large variety of products and large variability in order quantities, typical for companies with a large proportion of sub-contracted manufacture, it became impractical, and uneconomic, to compute an accurate cost estimate for each order. Because of the dominance of labour costs in the overall production costings, it became common and accepted practice to express production costs as summation of the aggregated material cost, estimated direct labour cost and a fixed multiplier of the direct labour cost, as a contribution to indirect costs.

With increasing mechanization the proportion of the cost of manufactured components due to direct labour costs has steadily fallen. This is due to several factors. With the reducing need for operatives to control the manufacturing processes directly, their effort could be distributed, e.g. with one machinist tending a number of machines rather than directly operating a single one. A complementary change is that an increasing number of personnel are necessarily required for the extremely skillful tasks of machine setting and machinery maintenance. The direct labour costs, in their turn, were often originally computed from standards which included generous allowances because of the intensive and arduous effort which was a feature of manufacturing systems with low rates of mechanization. With increasing mechanization, the trend is for direct labour activities to become less physically exacting than previously, although it is generally uncommon for standard performance data to be revised to take account of these changes. A common feature of manufacturing management in recent years has been the preoccupation of managers in reducing even further the direct labour costs. The (fallacious) rationale of this strategy is that, since product costs are expressed as a (often very large) multiple of labour costs, product costs can be reduced by attacking direct labour costs. (See Figure 6.1 and the analysis by Small [4,5]). The consequence of such a strategy, where it is feasible at all, is a further reduction of the proportion of direct labour costs and a corresponding further erosion of the realism with which the price to the customer reflects the actual manufacturing costs.

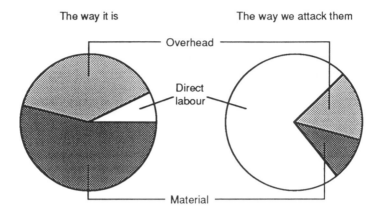

Figure 6-1. Losing Sight of the Problem (© IMechE 1983. Reproduced with permission)

If prices are based on inaccurate costings some products will be underpriced and some will be overpriced. The consequences, in an efficient market, are inescapable. Where goods are overpriced, competitors can provide products profitably at a lower price; where they are underpriced, competitors can stay out of the market leaving the enterprise trading at a loss. What saves many companies from insolvency is that their competitors are using equally inaccurate costing systems.

Equally serious is the effect of inaccurate costing systems on make-or-buy decisions. A common comparison is between factory cost, computed in the fashion described above, and a quotation from an external supplier who may have a number of reasons for a lower quotation. These include a corporate strategy for market penetration, which is not sustainable in the long-term (although Keynes warned that 'In the long run we are all dead' must be kept in mind), if it entails pricing at less than cost, and, more threateningly, a more realistic and rational costing structure. Every decision for external purchase reduces the production base over which the indirect costs are spread, and hence makes internal costs even more unrealistic and uncompetitive. A more rational make-or-buy decision criterion would be based on the comparison between the quotation and the marginal cost of increasing production – which in under-utilized systems is closer to the sum of the material and direct labour costs than to the computed aggregate production cost.

An extreme view, suggested by Yates [6], is that labour costs should now be treated as indirects. He cites examples such as the Apple Macintosh computer where labour costs constitute only 1% of overall manufacturing costs.

One example, which the author hopes is an extreme case, but fears is typical, was a company which was visited in 1985. To plan their work they were using standard method and machining data which they had inherited from the previous occupants of the factory, when it was returned to civilian use in 1946. This data had been obtained under the specialized manufacturing systems for production of weaponry. The products were significantly different in design and methods of manufacture. Many of the machines were, however, those which had been taken over in 1946.

On the revenue side the company was equally ignorant of the true income of the business. List prices were set at an arbitrary premium over the company's competitors, but with individual salespeople having a large degree of discretion as to discounts offered to the customers.

Different functional groups within the business each used different measures of the profitability of the enterprise. To some extent, this followed the (usually commendable) principle suggested earlier, that management should only be held responsible for factors within their domain of control. In this case, however, the financial data was so artificial that it was an endless source of interdepartmental tension. One typical example was a product listed at £100 but sold at a price of approximately £50 (taking into account the average level of discount). The budgetary control and reporting method used by the company gave a computed positive margin of £10 per unit. However, based on sales cost estimates, the company was, alternatively, making a loss of £5.

As has been suggested, at the time when the standard costing methodologies were developed, the expense of computing accurate costings for each order received by a company was prohibitive. This is now far from true with the availability of vast resources of computing power. Even though this power has been nominally available for perhaps twenty years, it is only the changes in the *distribution of computing resources* which has given the power to those who are capable of specifying the problems. Previously, in many companies, computer facilities had been the exclusive domain of the data processing specialists. As providers of centralized services, their priority was on the provision of large-scale integrated information systems, according to their own perception of the consensus of the best practice of the enterprise. In these circumstances, the natural inclination is to incorporate the procedures currently regarded as authoritative, i.e. the traditional cost accounting methodologies. Thus the tendency of the (essentially bureaucratic) data processing departments was to reinforce the (extremely unsatisfactory) status quo. This resistance to change was motivated by the defence of functional territory – preservation of power and status – but achieved this by exploiting the ignorance of the capability and promise of technology, which was aggravated by lack of training of middle and senior management.

The arrival of the personal computer has broken the stranglehold of centralist data processing departments on the management of information in companies. Equally important is the range of powerful, yet inexpensive, computer software. With the availability of spreadsheets and database management software, it becomes possible to compute production costings based on realistic values of labour, material and manufacturing costs.

At a higher level, Executive Information Systems and

Decision Support Systems enable Sensitivity Analysis and 'What If?' Analysis, for investigation of make-or-buy and other marginal costing decisions, with current cost values rather than indexed historical data. The technology has manifestly become available, and is being used, for the transition to Deal and Kennedy's [7] *atomised organization*, described earlier. The danger of this evolutionary development of the organization is that the corporate direction will be subverted and the enterprise fragmented into locally vigorous, but globally unfocussed – and ultimately unviable – units, with no consensus as to the overall direction of corporate strategy. (See Prahalad and Hamel [8]).

Justifying Investment in Manufacture

Investment in new manufacturing systems technology is often a triumph of faith over analytical judgement. Just as important in examining the validity of investment criteria, perhaps more so, are the investment project proposals which fail the standard financial performance tests of a business.

There are a number of industries where accepted standard tests of investment viability are extremely difficult to satisfy. Typical of these industries is the machine tool business. As described by Kuba [9] machine tool manufacture has typically a very low Return On Capital Employed (ROCE), but a very high Return On Sales volume (ROS). A further inhibition to the successful trading performance of machine tool builders is the relationship between the cycle of investment in production technology and the wider economic cycle.

Ideally, companies should invest in new production equipment immediately before a period of high demand in their industry. (Or, more precisely, the equipment should be installed and commissioned before the surge of demand). A much more common picture, however, is that companies only recognize the deficiencies of their existing manufacturing systems when they are approaching the height of a boom, and output is constrained by capacity or reliability problems. By the time that investment proposals are completed, the period of high demand may have passed and the urgency for investment is no longer a priority. Similar arguments apply to the planning of company training programmes where deficiencies become evident during periods of intensive production, when companies are least able to respond, but are seen as of much lower priority during troughs in the business cycle.

Such defects in the management of the investment cycle are symptoms of the ascendancy of pure financial measures over strategic planning processes, a practice which is confirmed by the analysis of Goold [10] and KPMG [11]. Some of the failures of corporate planning defy description. For example, Professor Chris Voss, of the London Business School, cited one example of a company which invested £100m in new production facilities without feeling it important to notify their production departments because the investment was 'confidential'. (Financial Times, 29th November 1989.)

There are two important issues in the justification of investment in Advanced Manufacturing Technology and Systems. Firstly, the choice of investment appraisal methodology and the way in which such information is managed. Secondly, equally important, is the scope and quality of the information which is used as input data for the chosen investment appraisal criterion.

In all financial criteria of investment appraisal a comparison of expenditure and revenues is compared. One of the most common decisions in the design of manufacturing systems is the choice between replacement of an existing machine by either a machine of similar specifications or one with a significantly more advanced design. As an example, consider the choice between simple replacement of a manual lathe and changing to a numerically-controlled machine.

Two factors make the comparison of these alternatives difficult – and this is a common and relatively straightforward example. Firstly, the cash flow profiles are strikingly different. Secondly, there is significantly greater uncertainty in the data for the more advanced machine.

The differences in the cost curve are attributable to a number of factors. Such machinery is likely to demand different services. Staff must be trained or re-trained, for machine setting, programming, servicing, etc. There will be a large initial effort to produce programmes for stock components and expense in test pieces and scrap. New tooling will, in all probability, be required. Once the machine is running to specification, however, comparative running costs are likely to be lower, since there will be much less intervention for gauging, etc., and operatives may be distributed across a number of machines. On the revenue curve, initial production rates will be low because of the need for training, production of test components, development of component programmes, etc. Once the initial period is over revenues are commonly superior to manual machines because of higher machine utilization. Comparative cash flow behaviour of traditional and advanced manufacturing technology is illustrated in Figures 6.2 and 6.3.

The simplest method of investment appraisal is the *payback period* method. This is the evaluation of the time elapsed before the cumulative costs are matched by the cumulative revenue. In the examples shown this can be read directly from the cash flow graph. As can be seen, investments in Advanced Manufacturing Technology, which implicitly entail a protracted installation and commissioning period, and a significant learning process, are always liable to perform poorly, in payback period terms, in comparison with investments which entail simple replacements of existing technology. The major flaw of the payback period method is that it is totally indifferent to the cash flows after the payback period has elapsed.

The next investment appraisal method, in order of complexity, is the evaluation of the *Net Present Value (NPV)* of the investment. This method aggregates the future cash flows,

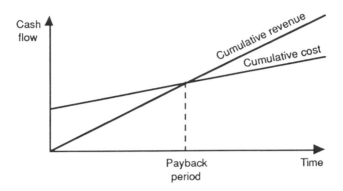

Figure 6-2. Cash Flow Profile for Replacement of Existing Production Technology

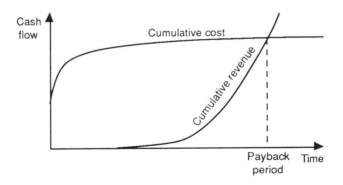

Figure 6-3. Cash Flow Profile for Introduction of Advanced Manufacturing Technology

discounted according to their time value. In contrast to the payback period method, this procedure takes into account all costs and revenues over the planning timescale of the investment, which is quite often less than the design life of the machine.

The *internal rate of return* method is a measure which is closely related to net present value. It corresponds to the computation of the rate of interest which would be appropriate for the project to just break even.

It is important to recognize that each of the methods described assesses a different aspect of the viability of the investment. Payback period is the most conservative measure and is an estimate of how long the business is exposed to the risk of the project; the Net Present Value is a measure of the anticipated overall benefit; the internal rate of return is a measure of the degree of deterioration which is tolerable in the financial climate before the project can be considered a loss. Many companies use all three measures.

It is often said of accountants that they can give a wrong answer with extreme precision. Investment appraisal methods which use probability measures to take account of uncertainty in discount rates or variability of the expected life of manufacturing plant have been available for some time (see, for example, Leech and Etemad [12]) but have not received general acceptance. It is interesting to note that the probability-based methods used by Leech and Etemad give some support for the more conservative investment appraisal procedures.

Each of the investment appraisal measures described above has its merits and applications. In what is generally accepted as an authoritative study, Professor Paul Marsh, of the London Business School, questions the strong, perhaps excessive, reliance of British and American companies on payback period methods. He cites a survey, by Barton et al [13], which suggests that payback criteria are actually becoming more popular (see Marsh [14]). It must be emphasized that payback methods are not, in themselves, undesirable, but their uncritical use and precedence over other criteria is evidence of short-term, and ultimately short-sighted, management policies.

Marsh takes issue with the view that Discounted Cash Flow (DCF) methods are subject to 'alleged anti-investment bias of the DCF technique itself'. He suggests that the influential American authors, Hayes and Garvin [15], who propound the view that there is 'a serious under-investment in the capital stock (the productive capacity, technology and workers' skills) on which {American} companies rest' are unjustified in attributing this to DCF per se, although it may be evidence that DCF may be 'being misapplied in practice '.

Where Marsh does see deficiencies in Discounted Cash Flow techniques is in the justifications for the type of linking of projects that is so typical of bridging the 'Islands of Automation' which constitutes the general integration of manufacturing systems:

> '...behind at least some of their (Hayes and Garvin) concerns, there is a deeper and more substantial worry which relates to the DCF technique itself. Most major long-term investments involve and indeed frequently open up a range and sequence of strategic options. Conventionally applied, DCF does not value options properly ..... Some writers have claimed that this has caused managers to under-invest in projects with a high option component (and hence, probably a high strategic value) because of their incorrect or incomplete financial analysis ...'

The context of investment in advanced manufacturing technology – whether operational, tactical or strategic – is illustrated in Figure 6.4. As has been mentioned, there is a considerable degree of discretion whether a Flexible Manufacturing System is justified in its entirety or as a sequence of purchases of individual machines.

There is little doubt that many of the strategic programmes which concern change in manufacturing systems fall into this category. Only by experimenting with Advanced Manufacturing Technology and its organization and control mechanisms can its full potential be identified and subsequently realized. Project proposers have the invidious choice between presenting their projects module by module, as they expect the implementation to

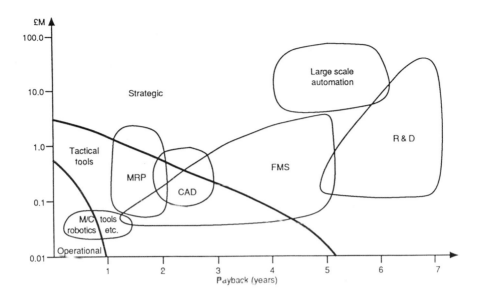

Figure 6-4. Costs and Benefits Compared (© IMechE 1986. Reproduced with permission)

take place, or bidding for the financial authority to carry out a coherent general strategy.

The inherent danger in portraying the investment programme in terms of the step-by-step approach is that initial learning costs must be loaded at the front end of the programme, leading to apparently excessive payback periods in the early projects and perhaps only marginally viable Net Present Values.

Bidding for capital investment in terms of an integrated manufacturing system is equally fraught with difficulties, although it is the preferred option of Small [4]. The magnitude of the financial commitment may be intimidatingly large, probably beyond the authority of the business unit management, and such a phased programme is also likely to transcend the planning horizon of the business unit. Once again, Marsh indicates the problems when authority for commitment of investment funds is vested in the corporate centre, whereas the source of strategic initiatives is almost invariably the divisions. Problems will be particularly acute in those enterprises which have deliberately restricted the capability of the corporate centre to intervene in business unit affairs by eliminating their management services role.

One partial solution to the problem of attributing costs to an individual project, which forms part of a larger programme, is the separation of expenditure which supports the general infrastructure of the business from those costs which are project-specific. In the example given above, familiarization with the operation of Advanced Manufacturing Technology, specifically the numerically controlled machines, can be considered as a 'core competency' of the business (in the terminology of Prahalad and Hamel [8]) and can quite legitimately be allocated to the general training budget of the organization.

A further difficulty recognized by Marsh [14] is the tendency for project management to seek to minimize the risks and exaggerate the benefits of their preferred investment option. He suggests that this may partially explain the tendency for senior management to set discount rates at levels above those prevailing in the markets. In comparisons of traditional and advanced technologies this is particularly pernicious, because high discount rates eliminate the advantage of the higher positive cash flows towards the end of the life of the project.

Quantifying Intangible Benefits

The introduction of Advanced Manufacturing Technology brings with it a number of benefits which are either novel, in which case comparison with existing systems may prove to be incompatible, or difficult to assign cash values, or may even be unforeseen. These may be classified into a number of categories:

- Benefits which are impossible to quantify.

- Benefits whose value can only be quantified subsequently, in the light of the experience gained.

- Benefits which cannot be quantified because collection of data is not cost-effective.

- Subjective benefits.

- Imaginary benefits.

These include, for example, improvements in quality, which result in reduced scrap and rework, which can be quantified – albeit rather speculatively, and simplification of the production control and quality assurance activities, to which it is much more difficult to assign a value, since it is an opportunity benefit based on the elimination of costs which may not be accessible, as they are commonly lumped into overheads.

Other benefits consistent with the introduction of Advanced Manufacturing Technology include:

- Faster response to market conditions.

- More reliable and shorter delivery times.

- Improved management control (Small [3]).

As has been suggested already, these factors are mutually dependent and reinforcing. Their aggregate effect is, as a consequence, difficult to predict precisely. The consensus of writers who have addressed the difficulties of integrating assessment of the intangible benefits into investment proposals is, however, that the accountancy criteria can be met, and should be, provided that the project is financially viable in the broadest sense. (Small [3,4], Kaplan [1,2], Canada [16], Choobineh [17], Suresh and Meredith [18] and Yates [6]). This was expressed succinctly by Hamblin and Hundy [19] in the following terms:

'While benefits of technologies such as FMS may not be straightforward to quantify ...., there is no reason why attempts should not be made to put figures to all of the factors which are claimed to be intangible and in many cases this can be done. .... If such factors remain intangible indefinitely, they are of no real assistance to engineers attempting to convince profit-centred financial colleagues of the merits of their case'.

Observance of accountancy measures in the short term should not deter longer term pressure for the balance between strategic and financial control processes to be changed (Goold [10]). Methodologies have long been available to integrate financial criteria into a more general decision-making environment but these methods have been difficult to present in the context of traditional investment appraisal methodologies. (See, for example, Easton [20] and Saaty [21]). The growing acceptance of more sophisticated software to aid decision making, from initial experience with spreadsheets to *Executive Information Systems*, *Decision Support Systems*, and ultimately *Intelligent Knowledge-Based Systems*, (Klein [22]) has raised the awareness amongst the financial community of the potential of these methods.

Financing Change

Notwithstanding the difficulties in the choice of investment appraisal methodologies and the inclusion of the intangible benefits, problems still remain as to the mechanism and sources for financing change. One of the problems of presenting the global programme of change, as recommended by Small [4], is that the costs and benefits are related according to Pareto principles, i.e. typically 80% of the overall benefit of the investment programme is likely to be attributable to only approximately 20% of the total investment. One of the key challenges, therefore, is the scheduling of the investment programme so that as much as possible of the later investment can be financed by gains from the earlier stages. The risks of premature termination of the programme when these early beneficial effects have been realized must also be appreciated.

The general premise of the current work is that most of the financial resources needed for funding change in manufacturing systems are already available within the organization, either as unnecessary inventory or by phasing programmes of change so that early changes rate highly in cost-benefit terms and later changes are financed from the proceeds of earlier changes. Where this is not possible, external resources must be obtained but the mechanisms almost invariably rely on the presentation of a business development plan covering the same issues as an internal justification.

The examples of best practice given by Hanson and Lucas, described ealier, where the performance of a business unit is measured against a plan relating the competitiveness of the business unit to other companies in its business sector, is rare. In their survey of strategic management, KPMG [11] found that in the manufacturing sector:

- 78% compared performance against their own previous performance.
- 71% compared performance against internal standards.
- 69% compared performance against company strategy.
- 44% compared performance against the overall business sector.
- 39% compared performance against key competitors.

The example of Courtaulds, given earlier, demonstrates the differing requirements for investment resources, and capability to satisfy them internally, of two divisions of the same company.

Each is competitive within its own sector but they cannot be subject to the same investment performance criteria. Marsh [14] cited differing levels of understanding of the operational activities of business units were a major cause of communication breakdowns between divisional management and the corporate centre. These differences in perceptions of the nature of the business were regarded by divisional management as an important factor in the quality of investment decision making.

One benefit which can be realized, in the overwhelming majority of manufacturing businesses, is the conversion of excess stock. In the case of Sheffield Forgemasters, described by van de Vliet [23], the 30000 tonnes of excess inventory generated £1.5m in the first ten days and £5m in three months.

Such realizations of excessive stock holdings are extremely typical. Alan Griffiths of Grant Thornton: 'We have managed to save businesses by getting them to reduce stocks. ... If you can get rid of £250000 from stocks of £500000 you can relieve your cash flow problems. If you have cash in the bank you will survive the recession. If you don't you are in trouble.'

The issues of management of working stocks are extremely complex and impinge on all functions of the business. From the accountancy point of view, maintenance of large stocks, whether as raw materials, work-in-progress or finished goods, represents a substantial opportunity cost, i.e. a reservoir of capital which, in all probability, could be put to far more productive use elsewhere in the business. Thus, although stocks usually appear in the balance sheet as an asset of the business, they are often indicative of a failure to exploit working capital of the enterprise to the full.

What is equally problematic, however, is how to measure the value of the stocks. The conservative approach, widely used among accountants, is to value stocks at the lower of cost or market value. A third option, which is not often used, perhaps regrettably, is valuation at scrap. With businesses with historically high working stocks even valuation at cost causes some difficulties, e.g. should material be valued at its original purchase price, which may have been some years ago, or at its replacement price?

The question must be addressed, however, of whether such financial windfalls should be fed back into investment in manufacturing systems. This is perhaps best answered using the criteria of Oscar Wilde's Lady Bracknell: for manufacturing management to lose 30000 tonnes of inventory may be regarded as a misfortune; to give them the proceeds looks like carelessness.

A more persuasive argument would be that if the excess stock were identified and quantified by the manufacturing departments, along with the strategy for realising the benefits, then it would be reasonable to incorporate inventory conversion into a broader programme of manufacturing systems investment.

As has been discussed earlier, some of the more radical reorganization strategies for manufacturing systems require minimal capital allocations. Typical cases being Group Technology and Kanban type (qv) production control systems. Inventory conversion has four primary aspects:

- Critical review of procurement policies.
- Elimination of unsaleable products in working inventories (scrap, obsolete, etc.).
- Completion of part-finished assemblies.
- Delivery of finished goods to customers.

In many respects, there is considerable merit in attacking the last two of these problems first. Examination of finished goods and those in final assembly will reveal a great deal about the health of the company's manufacturing systems. What is the quality of both performance to specification and finish of the deliverables? How much fitting is needed prior to final assembly? (Indicative of poor design for manufacture).

Company purchasing departments traditionally, and quite

properly, always try to take maximum advantage of discounting policies of the suppliers of raw materials and bought-in components. As a consequence many material stores are filled with a large quantity of material with poor stock turns (i.e. the number of times the value of material is used each year) whilst shortages occur fairly regularly for items with high (but perhaps irregular) stock turns. Even disregarding the storage and inventory holding cost of the low turnover items, the management disruption and other costs of emergency procurement of the shortage items are likely to outweigh the benefits of quantity discounting for the lower turnover items.

Two examples of industrial case studies will be discussed here. The first is from the author's own experience and the second is by Harvey-Jones [24].

In 1984 the author was asked to collaborate with a company in the building supplies industry. Although their product range was extremely wide, in terms of the number of catalogue items, each of their products was generically similar. The management were correctly and justifiably proud that they could make to order within a few days. Whilst this was undeniably true, a visit to their plant revealed a much wider picture. Their large stockyard was full, with an overflow on to the car park. Based on their own estimates, there appeared to be approximately a year's output in stock. Several of the bays in the stockyard were full of products which were painted a different colour to their regular stock. When asked whether these were customer specials, the manufacturing engineers replied that this was stock produced prior to their change of colour standard (approximately two years previously) but was otherwise functionally identical to their current stock products. Once incorporated into a building the colour was no longer visible. When questioned further as to why such anomalies had been allowed to develop, it appeared that the manufacturing engineers were reluctant to suggest the disposal of the obsolete stock because they did not wish to be seen to be responsible for writing down the assets of the business. Other options, such as holding a stocktaking sale (in the same way as high street retailers) or simply delivering the products to their customers just simply had not occurred to them. However the engineers had identified the problem, knew what the solution was, but did not have the courage of their convictions to force through the single logical solution.

Sir John Harvey-Jones has cited another similar example at the Morgan car company. The problem posed to Harvey-Jones was how to increase production '.... without risking Morgan's reputation for producing hand-built cars.' He recognized at an early stage that the company needed to increase its profitability to ensure its survival. One immediate and obvious inventory problem, which was already well-known to the company, was the fitting of engines to the chassis as early as possible in the production process. Not only did this tie up a huge amount of capital it actually interfered unnecessarily with the fitting of subsequent sub-assemblies. So not only could the company have realized a substantial amount of working capital by fitting the engines at a later stage, but it would also have simplified their production engineering.

Thus the rationalization of assembly can often be the most rewarding of activities in cost-benefit terms. Technologically, it is often the least sophisticated aspect of manufacturing operations. Because it has usually had least capital investment allocated to it, it has often had the least attention in terms of production engineering effort. Finally, all of the faults of previous production activities are evident.

In attacking procurement the minimization of inventories is again a priority. There is, once again, a considerable degree of merit in using a Pareto based approach, categorizing components into 'A', 'B' and 'C' categories corresponding to their value. Typically Pareto A items are the major purpose-designed components, Pareto B are intermediate value components, perhaps conforming to industry standards, and Pareto C items are generic components.

Particularly beneficial are the results of applying *value engineering* techniques to the Pareto A items. Value engineering is a long-established methodology but, as remarked by Hill [25], has not received the recognition it deserves:

'An important, but often under-used, technique to help provide (a) systematic approach to reducing the cost of a product or service but without impairing its function is value analysis. It is concerned with the methodical examination of each product, component or service with the purpose of minimizing its cost without reducing its functional value.'

Value analysis and value engineering are often used synonymously. The former term is used rather more generally to cover the criticism of general approaches to the provision of goods and services, whilst value engineering refers more narrowly to the assurance of conformance of products to their specifications at minimum cost.

The works of two pioneers of value analysis, Miles [26] and Gage [27], is still as fresh today as when it was first presented. The rationale of value analysis was made by Miles in the following terms:

'On average, one fourth of manufacturing cost is unnecessary. The extra cost continues because of patterns and habits of thought, because of personal limitations, because of difficulties in promptly disseminating ideas and because today's thinking is based on yesterday's knowledge.' (Quoted in Hill [25]).

In the Morgan case, each product variant has a different chassis or bodywork (emphatically A category items) for no better reason, apparently, than the fact that customers (according to the company's mythology) see the idiosyncratic variances as desirable. The same internal perception of the desirability of product differentiation at ERF was found to be fallacious and inhibiting to change. In contrast to Morgan, however, ERF recognized that product rationalization was the key to their survival. Because of the lack of standardization of the Pareto A items at Morgan there was a concomitant, and unnecessary, differentiation of the B type items, which could otherwise be standardized. Furthermore, whereas fasteners and other small components would usually be type C components, with this lack of value engineering there is likely to be a proliferation of special fasteners for such applications.

In a value engineering exercise undertaken by the author and associates (reported in Ajderian, Brandon and Frankland [28]) the following benefits were achieved in a power transmission coupling range which a company had identified as central to their business strategy:

- Replacement of 11 products with 8.

- Machining from bar rather than castings (Pareto A).

- Replacement of 7 pin-buffer sets with 3 (Pareto B).

- To use standard heavy duty bolts rather than company specials for pins (Pareto B becomes Pareto C).

- To replace 2 unsymmetrical components with a pair of symmetrical components (Pareto A).

This analysis suggested that financial benefits would be gained:

- Once only: 44% reduction in Pareto A inventory value.

- Recurrent: 28% reduction in material costs.
  19% reduction in machining costs.

Relevance Regained – Activity Costing Procedures

As has been discussed, Johnson and Kaplan [3] described how a series of independently logical steps led to an illogical system of management accountancy. The availability of substantial databases of records of manufacturing information enables an approach to management accounting known as Activity Based Costing. As with many other TLAs (Three Letter Acronyms), denoting Activity Based Costing as 'ABC' has already caused widespread confusion, since Activity Based Costing is often used with Pareto analysis – which already has a generally accepted useage for its A, B and C categories.

Activity Based Costing is already being vigorously marketed by a number of major consultancies. As with all such marketing campaigns, the current perception of the successful performance of Activity Based Costing, which is generally well deserved, is likely to be prejudiced by inappropriate application by incompetent or unscrupulous consultants and by its adoption by organizations in search of a 'quick fix'.

Activity Based Costing has been described by Innes and Mitchell [29], in a report for the Chartered Institute of Management Accountants. This report contains case studies of two manufacturing enterprises and a retail organization.

References

[1] Kaplan, R. S., "Yesterday's accounting undermines production", *Harvard Business Review*, July-August 1984, pp95-101.
[2] Kaplan, R. S., "Must CIM be Justified by Faith Alone?", *Harvard Business Review*, March-April 1986, pp87-94.

[3] Johnson, H. T. and Kaplan, R. S., *Relevance Lost: The Rise and Fall of Management Accounting*, Harvard Business School Press, Boston, MA 1987.

[4] Small, B. W., "Paying for the Technology – Making the Intangibles Tangible", *Second European Conference on Automated Manufacturing*, Editor Rooks B.W., 1983a, 183-187.

[5] Small, B. W., "Wealth Generation – Our Essential Task", *Proceedings of the Institution of Mechanical Engineers*, Part B, Volume 197, 1983b, pp131-141.

[6] Yates, A., "Evaluation of Advanced Manufacturing Technology", in *Managing Advanced Manufacturing Technology*, editor Voss C.A., IFS/Springer Verlag, Bedford, England, 1986, pp225-239.

[7] Deal, T. and Kennedy, A., *Corporate Cultures: The Rites and Rituals of Corporate Life*, Addison-Wesley, New York 1982.

[8] Prahalad, C. K. and Hamel, G., "The core competence of the corporation", *Harvard Business Review*, May-June 1990, pp79-91.

[9] Kuba, Y., *Master of Manufacturing Technology; the 70 Year History of MAZAK*, N D Publications, Tokyo 1989.

[10] Goold, M. (with Quinn, J. J.) *Strategic Control: Milestones for Long-term Performance*, The Economist Books /Hutchinson, London 1990.

[11] *Information for Strategic Management: A Survey of Leading Companies, 1990*, KPMG Peat Marwick Management Consultants, London 1990.

[12] Leech, D.J. and Etemad, F., "Paying for Equipment", *Chartered Mechanical Engineer*, January 1984 pp43-45.

[13] Barton, H., Brown, D., Cound, J. and Willey, K., "Decision Processes for Strategic Capital Investment Within UK-Based Diversified Industry", MBA Project Report, London Business School, May 1989.

7

Exploiting Resources to the Full

Undertaking programmes of change in manufacturing systems entails the solution of diverse and interdependent technological and managerial problems of daunting complexity. Difficulties are likely to be accentuated by shortages of the necessary resources, both in terms of finance and of trained manpower, which are liable to increase the load, and hence aggravate the management problems further. As a consequence the identification and optimum exploitation of existing resources is often the most urgent and potentially rewarding of management tasks.

There have been numerous surveys of the performance of manufacturing industry, from a wide variety of perspectives. Wherever these surveys compare the performance of the most successful users of a new management technique or new production technology with that of other users, the use of human resources is a key discriminator. (See, for example, Waterlow and Monniot [1] or Ingersoll Engineers [2]). As can be seen from the survey data presented in Figure 7.1. Human relations and training were regarded extremely highly in successful implementation of cellular manufacturing systems.

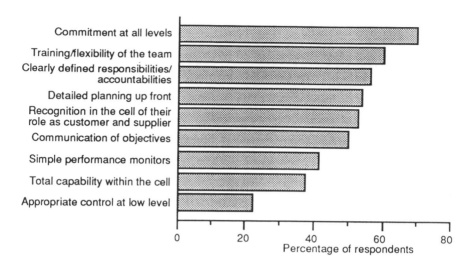

Figure 7-1. Factors Rated Most Important for Successful Cells (© Ingersoll Engineers Ltd. Reproduced with permission)

Skill Inventory

The most valuable resources of any organization are its employees. Without an appropriately skilled, and perhaps more importantly motivated, workforce it is purely specious to invest in new machinery or operating systems.

As with investment in plant and machinery, skill resources can best be augmented by comparing the existing corporate skill profile with that regarded as necessary or desirable to achieve the corporate strategy. As with investment in Advanced Manufacturing Technology, described in the last chapter, it is often only after the initial stages of implementation of a strategy that it becomes apparent what resources are needed for later parts of the plan. Consider, for example, a conclusion of Waterlow and Monniot [1]:

'Companies with a successful integrated CAPM system had generally invested heavily in internal education courses for staff at all levels. Although these courses were regarded as crucial, anecdotal evidence implied that the real understanding of a CAPM system came from its practical use over an extended period.'

Thus human resource planning should become a continuous and standard element of the corporate strategy of the enterprise. Applying a financial planning metaphor, a skill shortfall can be identified as the variance between the desired skill profile and existing resources.

Again anologous with investment planning, the best resources are those which are generated internally. (Prietula and Simon [3]). As with product inventories, valuable resources are likely to be unrecorded and unrecognized, and hence neglected. Skills which were a priority when staff were recruited may have been allowed to atrophy and new skills may have been acquired subsequently, perhaps without the knowledge of the company, for example computer expertise acquired by hobbyists. Even activities such as part-time degree courses relevant to company operations may be concealed from senior management, particularly in companies where training is perceived as having a low status. The first priority, therefore, is to record and assess in-house expertise. In accordance with the cost accounting analogy used here it is appropriate to describe this as skill stock-taking.

Skill stock-taking can be taken in two ways depending on how it is seen by the workforce. This, in its turn, is dependent on the history of industrial relations in the enterprise. Where there is a predominantly adversarial industrial relations environment, and perhaps more particularly in the industries with declining workforces, skill stock-taking is likely to be regarded with suspicion, which is understandable in the context of those companies reducing their workforce seeking to retain the most skilled personnel. Once again, both bad practice and good are self-reinforcing. If staff are convinced that enhancement of the overall level of skill in the organization is to their benefit, and that they will be given personal opportunities from the skill stock-taking exercise, either in terms of job enrichment or career advancement (or both), then success is assured.

This is a key issue in the management of change in manufacturing systems. The priorities of training and of communication of objectives are two of the key discriminators between the most successful companies and those whose performance is less impressive. (See, for example, Ingersoll Engineers [2]).

The Oliver Wight group of companies are specialists in the use of Manufacturing Resource Planning systems (MRP II (qv)). They classify users by an A-D scale and note that 'Class A users spend twice as much on education as did the D users.' Walter Goddard [4], President of Oliver Wight Education Associates, remarked that the attitude:

'... what's needed is better software, a larger computer, more terminals, i.e., more money.'

is a myth, and that:

'The Class A users are not distinguished by spending more money. The major difference between the worst and the best is two words – understanding and attitude. If the general manager has the correct understanding of MRP II and a "can do" attitude to become Class A, you'll succeed.'

Without reliance on detailed survey data, the anecdotal evidence suggests that companies fall into two simple categories where technical training is concerned. Put simply, there are a relatively small group of companies, called here the training companies, who demonstrate total commitment to training their workforce, whilst the much larger remainder, the non-training companies, rely on recruitment from the training companies to fill shortfalls in their skill inventory. Once again the survey data, shown in Figure 7.2, reveal substantial disparities between the priority given to enhancing the performance of the workforce in the most successful companies as compared to their competitors.

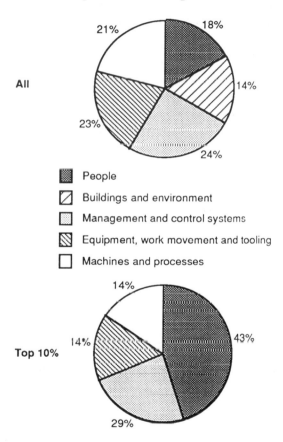

Figure 7-2. Comparative Percentage Allocation of Significant Investment (© Ingersoll Engineers Ltd. Reproduced with permission)

One penalty which the non-training companies have to pay is that the training given is that which suits the training company, and not that which meets their own strategic needs. Many of the training companies are concentrated in the aerospace and defence industries which operate in a markedly different commercial environment to the consumer-oriented enterprise. Project timescales differ greatly, the profit basis is often 'cost-plus', i.e. the customer covers project costs plus a fixed notional profit margin; product specifications are all too often open ended, leading to disputes on conformance failures; quality often implies unreasonable expectations of operational performance regardless of the cost implications. As might be expected, many of the habits absorbed in these environments have to be 'unlearned' when engineers move to organizations with different profit objectives, market environments and corporate strategies.

A further inherent problem, in the recruitment of ready trained staff from other companies, is that the staff who wish to move are those whom the training company find least attractive for future employment. There is substantial circumstantial evidence that training companies deliberately over-recruit, relying on the inevitable wastage of personnel to select for retention, by default, those who identify with the company's corporate culture. Since many of the training companies are rather bureaucratic and centralist, those who do not fit into the corporate culture, and frequently leave towards the end of their formal training period, or shortly after, are often the more entrepreneurially oriented employees who are uncomfortable in the large organization but are likely to fit well into the less structured environment of the small market oriented enterprise.

Notwithstanding the comments on the dangers of appointment of staff from outside the enterprise, new employees often bring new perspectives and insights on the management of a company's manufacturing systems. For example, Ingersoll Engineers [2] suggest that the trend to cellular manufacturing may have been enabled to a great extent by migration of engineers with familiarity with cellular manufacturing into companies without such experience. Furthermore it would be unwise, bordering on the negligent, to delay attacking urgent management problems until sufficient expertise had been generated internally.

As has already been suggested, D T N Williamson is one of the most creative engineers of the twentieth century. His proposed solution to the problem of the training imbalance was to accept, and exploit, the status quo by designating the committed training companies as *'Teaching Companies'*, in much the same way as the Teaching Hospitals train medical staff, by the establishment of centres of best practice, and to reward them by subsidizing their training activities.

The Teaching Company programme was taken up by the UK Science Research Council and the Department of Industry in the mid 1970s. Although it has performed a valuable role, particularly in technology transfer into small enterprises, it no longer conforms to Williamson's model.

One serious problem, of the reliance of non-training companies on others to provide them with skilled personnel, is that a number of the industries where training was historically of a high priority have been the 'smokestack' industries which have experienced the greatest decline in employment, with a corresponding reduction in their needs for newly trained personnel. In addition to the defence and aerospace industries, already mentioned, other examples include the steel industry, shipbuilding and mining. Thus the supply of trained staff on the open market can no longer be guaranteed. Furthermore, the inevitable result of demand exceeding supply in economic systems is that prices rise. Perhaps not before time, relative increases in skilled engineering salaries have consistently outperformed other industrial disciplines for some years.

Using the cost accounting metaphor, recruitment strategies correspond to make-or-buy decisions. When used to excess, external recruitment can erode both the ability of the organization to enhance its capability profile internally, by eroding the habits of continuous training, and also the self esteem, and subsequently the morale, of the indigenous workforce, as they perceive that their skills are not valued.

Thus the development of a training culture within an organization is likely to be an essential feature of a long-term survival strategy. Skill stock-taking may well reveal immediate requirements for long-term specialist skills which cannot be satisfied from internal resources within an acceptable timescale. In such circumstances there is no alternative to recruitment from outside, but this should be regarded as the exception rather than the rule for sustained growth of the enterprise.

The definition of what qualifies as training should be interpreted in its broadest sense. As with advertising – where it is said that there is no such thing as bad publicity – it is hard to imagine any sort of training which will be bad for business.

Sources of Short-term Support

A comprehensive skills inventory exercise is likely to reveal some managerial tasks which are beyond the capability of the existing management but with relatively short durations. In such circumstances it is both natural and desirable to complement in-company expertise with outside specialists.

As will be seen, in the case study on production control in the small company, consultants can provide a valuable short-term resource for the management of the company when they are under pressure during a period of change. However, care must be taken that a dependency culture is not established, where the company's management invariably look to outside consultants for support for long-term problems which should be the concern of strategic management within the enterprise. (Brandon [5] and Prahalad and Hamel [6]).

References

[1] Waterlow, J. G. and Monniot, J. P., *A Study of the State of the Art in Computer-Aided Production Management in UK Industry*, ACME Directorate, Science and Engineering Research Council, Swindon, England, April 1986.

[2] *Competitive Manufacturing the Quiet Revolution: A Survey of Implementation and Performance across British Manufacturing Industry*, Ingersoll Engineers, Rugby, England, 1990.

[3] Prietula, M. J. and Simon, H. A., "The Experts in Your Midst", *Harvard Business Review*, January-February 1989, pp120-124.

[4] Goddard, W. E., "Control of the Business", *Oliver Wight Companies Newsletter*, Newbury, New Hampshire 1985.

[5] Brandon, J. A., "Where Consultants Fall Down", *Management Today*, May 1988, pp109-119.

[6] Prahalad, C. K. and Hamel, G., "The core competence of the corporation", *Harvard Business Review*, May-June 1990, pp79-91.

8

A Case Study: Production Control in the Small Company

There is a wide variety of reasons why companies should review the effectiveness of their chosen production control strategy on a regular basis. These include changing markets, developments in management theory, improved production technology and advances in information technology.

Production control is a crucial subsystem within the overall framework of a manufacturing company's management information system. Without an effective production control system the company cannot function adequately. The development of a good production control system is a classic example of the old adage: 'It's simple but it's not easy'.

It is not intended that this case study should provide a definitive exposition on production control. Indeed there are a number of good texts available already, for example Corke [1]. What is intended is to offer a general outline of some current themes in production control and some guidelines on avoiding the common pitfalls.

Scope: Production Control, CAPM and CIM

Production control is a term which has rather traditionalist overtones. It takes account of the historical functional divisions within a company and, in many organisations, is carried out primarily by clerical staff, treating production machines and processes as 'black boxes'. Similarly, in many engineering companies the production manager has no formal technical qualification, production engineering being a separate function, with perhaps both managers reporting to a manufacturing manager.

The historical divisions are gradually being eroded. Successful manufacturing organizations of the future will be structured in terms of an integrated system of design, planning, automation and control. The traditional function of production control will be subsumed within Computer-Assisted Production Management (CAPM). This in its turn will contribute to the overall Computer-Integrated Manufacture (CIM), coupled for example with CAD/CAM systems and financial and quality utilities. It is necessary in the specification of the CAPM system to consider the system interfaces to the other elements of CIM. However Waterlow and Monniot [2] observe:

'Most UK companies (other than the few manufacturing systems-oriented ones) were not thinking seriously about links between CAPM and the other elements in CIM.'

The particular danger which may prevent the incorporation of CAPM into CIM relates to the traditional position of production control within the area of general management. It would be quite likely that senior management would rely heavily on the advice of their data processing managers. The natural choice for most DP managers would be a package, probably written in COBOL, which was developed and mounted on a traditional DP machine, using the manufacturer's proprietary operating system. In contrast many of the other elements of CIM are developed by and for engineers. They are usually written in FORTRAN or ALGOL derived languages, on computers with a different style of operating system. Thus a plan for CIM must recognise that system integration is dependent on the communication capability of the subsystems in terms of data structures, operating systems and communications protocols. Waterlow and Monniot [2] suggest:

'Leading edge companies appear to be having difficulty in addressing CAPM within a CIM framework. This may be because CAPM takes a "top-down" business approach to systems integration, whereas the majority of other CIM systems are evolving from the "bottom-up in business terms"'.

It should be further emphasized that a major danger for companies without significant in-house computer experience is the dependence on a particular hardware configuration, operating system or proprietary software. This is known, quite accurately, as "locking in".

The Developing Company: A Common Profile

It is unlikely that a successful small company, planning for expansion, will have sufficient spare manpower/resources to undertake the design and implementation of a new production control system from scratch. Such enterprises are often working already at the limits of the capability of their management. In such circumstances it is not unusual for the overall management information system to grow organically, to the point where it is beyond the comprehension of any one individual. Each function will assess overall system performance on the basis of its own priorities and perceptions. Each will require differing data and use different criteria to form their own performance measures. For example general budgetary activities may base cash flow assessment on the product of delivered volume by a notional average product price whereas this would be an unsatisfactory measure for audit purposes. Differing criteria of the functions lead to conflicts over priorities for maintenance of accurate data; a key aspect being the time delay between generation and incorporation of data into the database. Often the delay is dependent on the perceived urgency to the department concerned which may lead to variations in the period of updating files and hence to conflicting records. At this stage individual managers are likely to take action to maintain the integrity of their own benchmark data. It is likely that ostensibly common data is duplicated in different formats and becomes corrupt.

The symptoms of this system degradation are widely known for example:

- Quoted price is based on historical data with allowances for inflation and becomes progressively detached from actual costs. Some products are inadvertently produced at a loss, whilst others are overpriced and uncompetitive.

- Sales staff have no data on the current production schedule and make unrealistic delivery promises, undermining customer satisfaction.

- Production schedules take no account of stock shortages, leaving a large element of un-kitted work in progress.

- Continuation of issue of jobs until the shop is so full that no further work can be issued.

- Allowing shopfloor supervision, progress chasers etc to vary the schedule to match their own (often extremely parochial) perception of production targets.

- Failure to record scrap and rework.

Unfortunately by the time that these symptoms show themselves the company is already likely to be in some difficulty. Remedial effort must necessarily take place whilst the operations of the company continue. The twin problems of poor working practices and faulty production data are mutually dependent and must be tackled together, otherwise the programme will be useless.

The temptation is to attempt to introduce a new system, replacing the existing system (or lack of it!), in the mistaken belief that nothing can make matters worse. The most likely result is that the new system will replace the existing small amount of inaccurate, incomplete or contradictory data with an overwhelming quantity of unfamiliar, but equally useless data. This would be particularly true when manual procedures are replaced with a computerized system.

The experience described above is common but by no means universal. A successful implementation of an integrated production control system, in a developing company, has been described by the author and co-workers elsewhere (Thomas et al [3]). The key to the success of this project can be summarized as follows:

- All members of the company staff knew and understood the operation and significance of the control procedures which applied to them.

- Procedures were regularly reviewed and any judged non-essential eliminated.

- The overall control system was structured in a modular fashion to ensure that intervention to modify data was restricted to a single function.

- The control of data was restricted to identified functional authorities.

- Access to the data was made as wide as possible, subject to normal considerations of commercial confidentiality, to eliminate the danger of the establishment of unofficial archives.

It should be noted that, in the project just described, the company gave considerable weight to the importance of using the opportunity to overhaul traditional methods and reconsider basic business objectives.

Fads and Panaceas

It is not unusual for new production control strategies to be introduced during a period of corporate crisis. It may well be that the most obvious symptoms of the company's problems may be linked to deficiencies of production control, for example late deliveries, high work in progress, production shortages, armies of progress chasers but very little progress etc. The sudden introduction of new, untried and unfamiliar procedures are, however, likely to exacerbate rather than ameliorate these problems. Even bad systems have a degree of intrinsic stability which it may be dangerous to disturb unless the consequences of the changes can be foreseen and quantified. One of the most surprising features of bad industrial management control systems is their robustness and tolerance of misuse. The management effort of the introduction of the new system, coupled with the unpredictable behaviour of the residue due to the old system, is likely to place an intolerable load on the resources of the company.

A further problem of introducing a new production control system in a period of crisis is the vulnerability of the management to choice of an inappropriate system. Production control, like any other discipline, is subject to fads and fashion. One mistake which is easy to make is to assume that a computer-based production control system is automatically preferable to a manual system. One of the successes of the Japanese approach to production control is the recognition that in many applications a well planned manual system has significant advantages over a computer based system. Indeed the widely discussed KANBAN system achieves effective production control by eliminating the need for computer control of shop loading. It should be noted, however, that KANBAN systems are only applicable for a restricted range of product types (in terms of restricted ranges and demand cycles particularly).

Self Awareness

As with any other problems in engineering, introduction or modernization of a production control system requires:

- Definition of the problem.
- Analysis of options.
- Definition of a programme.
- Setting objectives.
- Implementation.
- System maintenance.

Whether the solution process is carried out in-house or contracted to external consultants, the company must specify the problem, decide on timescales and allocate resources, either in terms of finance or manpower, for system design, implementation and maintenance.

As will be discussed, there are a number of good reasons why a company should use consultants in the design and installation of new production control systems. It should always be kept in mind however that it is the client who has the long term interest in the successful outcome of the project. The client will have the task of operation and maintenance of the system after the departure of the consultant. Consequently the project plan should include a clear and thorough assessment of the skills and resources necessary to operate the system and include a detailed training programme for the company's staff. The skill needs for successful CAPM implementation are frequently underestimated. In the survey by Waterlow and Monniot [2] eleven out of the twenty-nine companies studied cited skill shortages as the main problem in introducing CAPM.

There are a number of publications available specifically designed as self help guides for CAPM implementation, for example the brief guide by Cumbers and Tomes [4]. Particularly useful is the self assessment questionnaire which forms a major part of the guide. Many consultancy organisations also provide such guides, often free, which are of a similar format. Whilst the motives for distribution of these publications are far from altruistic, the tracts themselves are helpful, thorough, professionally prepared and in the author's experience objective. The intention on the consultancy's part is to provide an introduction to the company and its services in the expectation of future business. There are several instances of consultancies successfully entering into publishing as a natural progression from what were essentially promotional publications such as these.

Whether a consultancy is used or not, the first stage of any programme of modernization of methods should be an analysis of the current system, identifying its strengths and weaknesses, noting particularly duplication, conflicts or inconsistencies in both data and procedures.

Maximum use should be made of the opportunity to learn from the experience of others. Particularly useful are the awareness programmes organised by government agencies, trade associations and professional institutions. These schemes allow visits to demonstration companies who are prepared to discuss their own experience in implementation of new technology.

It is likely that the self awareness exercise will reveal substantial need for staff training in the majority of companies. This should include not only specific training to enable implementation of the chosen production control system but also studies to support strategic planning.

Planning for Change

Few companies will be able to afford the luxury of introducing a new production control system in isolation from their other management activities. Thus a strategy must be devised such that:

- Key personnel are available when required.

- The old control system can be operated whilst the new system is being installed.

- The data entry for the new system is sufficiently flexible to maintain data integrity during changeover.

The natural consequence of these considerations is that a modular approach is almost invariably used, both in system design and also in implementation. This holds the implicit danger of conflict and fragmentation in planning and difficulties in system integration, if the control procedures and the interfaces between functional interests are not agreed and applied.

An essential feature of the design of a system which influences most, if not all, of a company's operations, is the appointment of a system design authority. The role of the system design authority should be:

- To develop the overall system specification, to meet requirements specifications provided by user departments.

- To identify and resolve inconsistencies between different user requirement specifications.

- To allocate control restrictions and access limitations.

- To implement agreed system procedures.

- To maintain the system in operation.

- To review the system specification against changing needs.

Waterlow and Monniot [2] reported that user led system implementations were considerably more successful than those imposed by central authorities.

'All the 'finance'-led systems were unsuccessful..'

All of the CAPM suppliers and experienced users in the survey expected manufacturing control to be progressively decentralised.

Anticipating the Pitfalls

One of the most depressing features of providing academic support to industry is the regularity with which one encounters the same elementary problems. That is not to say that the academic, placed under the same pressures and constraints, would not fall into precisely the same ruts! Perhaps the most significant problem is that of neglect of long-term planning in favour of day-to-day firefighting. The introduction of such a new management procedure must, however, entail a commitment to long-term planning, indeed failure to define requirements was identified, by the consultancies in Waterlow and Monniot's survey [2], as the principal reason for the lack of success in CAPM. They further stressed that:

'.. the design of manufacturing systems required a company to have a coherent manufacturing strategy'.

Ideally the system implementation manager should be an existing functional manager in the company, with the consequent understanding of both the formal and informal aspects of the existing procedures. Too often when this occurs however the project manager of the system retains a role within the original department, leading to conflicts between long- and short-term planning. The natural consequence is the detriment of the system design role. Thus the person entrusted with the system design authority should be relieved of line management responsibilities.

The Benefits

The degree of benefit from CAPM is difficult to quantify in financial terms (as indeed is CIM in general). Reports of research into CIM in general often refer to "intangible benefits". This expression recognises that the majority of benefits are not amenable to the type of quantification necessary for the type of traditional payback analysis used to justify investment.

Although difficult to estimate, there will undoubtedly be some direct financial benefit from a variety of sources. It will no longer be necessary to use progress chasers to locate and expedite late orders, saving either their salaries or redeploying them to wealth-generating activities. More reliable schedules eliminate the need for excessive safety stocks and work in progress, giving direct benefits in inventory cost but in addition eliminating queues on the shopfloor.

The primary benefit, and perhaps the least tangible, is the change in the nature of control. Emphasis in management meetings changes from preoccupation with firefighting towards the consideration of strategic planning issues.

Package or Bespoke?

This is perhaps the most crucial question in choosing a new production control system. Reported user experience is rather confusing. Novice users have reported success in using

that machine tools of outstanding quality could only be produced on even better machines.

Unfortunately the installation performance of Japan's competitors has assisted them immensely. For example, British import and export records over a considerable number of years show that Britain is not only trading down in its manufactured goods but is importing production technology which is inferior to that which is being installed by its competitors. Thus, instead of setting out to compete with the best, Britain is trading down in the quality of its manufacturing systems, to the point where it is vulnerable to competition from the less industrialized countries where typical labour costs are lower. To make matters worse, all too often the equipment which is installed is not properly maintained and serviced.

There are a number of different facets of quality of investment in manufacturing systems which should be taken into account. These include the planning and implementation of the outcome of the strategic control process. As described by Hayes and Jaikumar [1], the context of investment strategy in production technology must be determined before satisfactory specifications for the manufacturing systems can be developed.

What has also become evident, in the research undertaken in the writing of the current volume, is that the acceptance of *islands of automation* appears to be a natural stage in the operation of many manufacturing systems based enterprises. They appear to reach a *plateau of experience* where they pause to assess progress and regroup, for perhaps some considerable time, prior to progressing to full integration. In the case of cellular manufacturing it seems that this process may take decades. To some extent this is explainable by the Pareto effect, whereby the benefits of grouping individual machines are extremely large in comparison to the effort expended, whereas the continuation to complete integration may appear to involve substantial additional expenditure with few immediate benefits. Thus the final integration can only be justified in strategic terms.

For these reasons many of the initiatives of government agencies, trade associations and professional organizations are viewed as a failure when the latent benefits are concealed, perhaps to reappear many years later, as is undoubtedly the case with group technology. This state of apparent dormancy is currently affecting the Manufacturing Automation Protocol and Technical Office Protocol (MAP/TOP). For example, the British Department of Industry has recently closed down its COMCENTRE which was dedicated to installation of networking technologies in manufacturing systems. Although the MAP/TOP standard may reappear in a more advanced form, there is no doubt that the eventual benefits of linking the islands of automation will, once again, be seen as a key strategic objective.

A key theme of the current work is that we should learn from the example of the great manufacturing engineers such as Ford, Honda and Ohno. These men have several things in common:

- Constant awareness of the three essential aspects of manufacturing: quality, price and delivery;

- A willingness to learn from their mistakes;

- The courage of their convictions;

- Superhuman reserves of perseverence.

Once these are instilled into the workforce of the manufacturing enterprise, the rest is easy!

References

[1] Hayes, R. H. and Jaikumar, R., "Manufacturing's Crisis: New Technologies, Obsolete Organizations", *Harvard Business Review*, September-October 1988, pp77-85.

[2]   Garnett, N., "Traditional virtues of long-term investment", *Financial Times*, January 19 1990.

[3]   Schonberger, R. J., "Frugal manufacturing", *Harvard Business Review*, September-October 1987, pp95-100.

[4]   Ashton, J. E. and Cook F. X. Jr, "Time to Reform Job Shop Manufacture", *Harvard Business* Review, March-April 1989, pp106-111.

[5]   Prahalad, C. K. and Hamel, G., "The core competence of the corporation", *Harvard Business Review*, May-June 1990, pp79-91.

[6]   Gill, A. K., "Engineers Matter – The Lucas key to international success", *Proceedings of the Institution of Mechanical Engineers*, Series B, 1986, pp205-213.

[7]   *Competitive Manufacturing the Quiet Revolution: A Survey of Implementation and Performance across British Manufacturing Industry*, Ingersoll Engineers, Rugby, England 1990.

[8]   Morone, J., "Strategic Use of Technology", *California Management Review*, Summer 1989, pp91-110.

[9]   Foster, R. N., *Innovation: the Attackers Advantage*, Macmillan London 1986.

[10] Kuba, Y., *Master of Manufacturing Technology: the 70 Year History of MAZAK*, N D Publications, Tokyo 1989.